D1236838

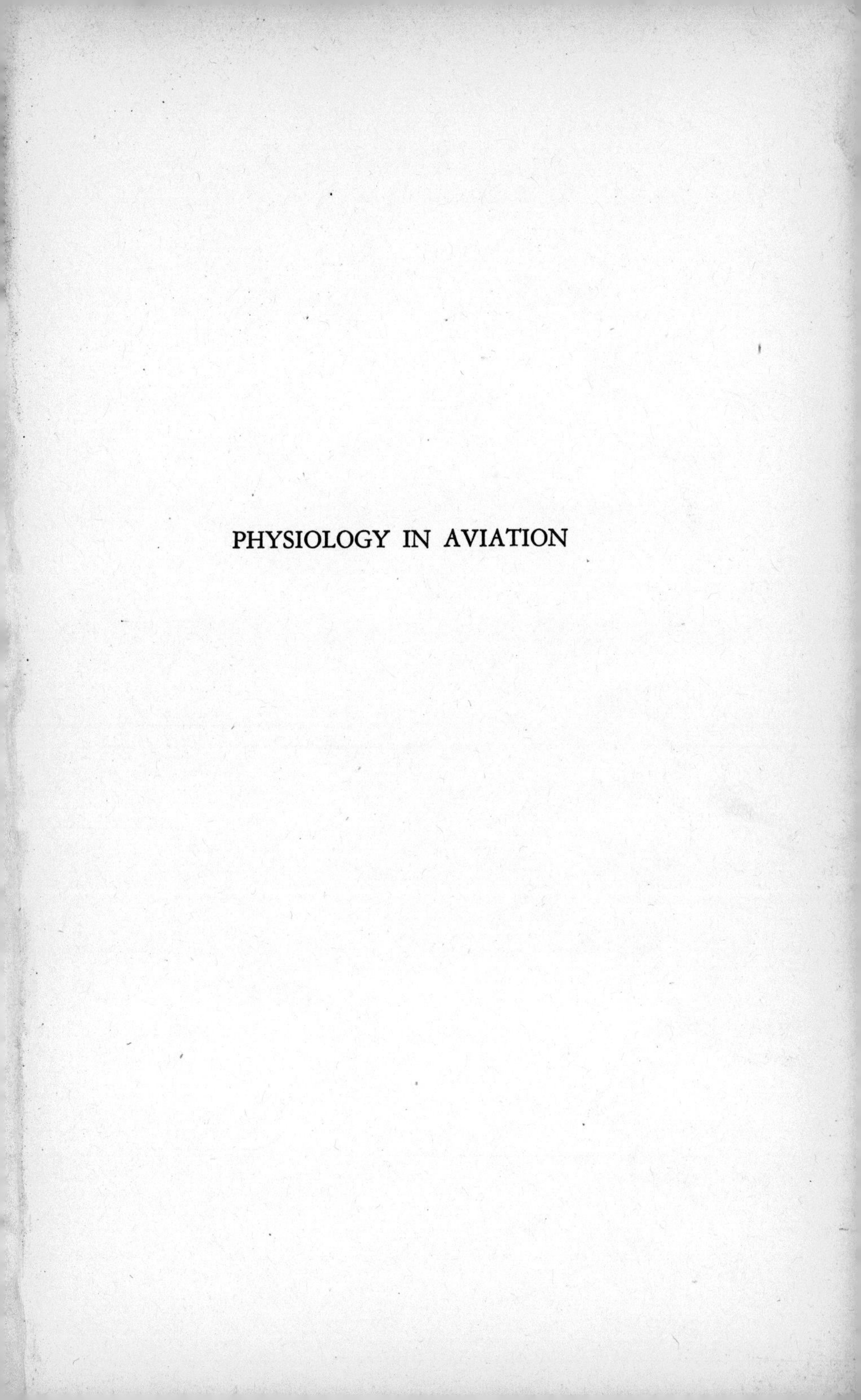

PHYSIOLOGY IN AVIATION

PHYSIOLOGY IN AVIATION

By

CHALMERS L. GEMMILL, B.S., M.D.

Commander, MC, USNR
Associate Professor in Physiology,
Johns Hopkins University, School of Medicine,
Baltimore, Maryland.
Instructor in Physiology, School of Aviation Medicine,
Naval Air Station, Pensacola, Florida.

1943

CHARLES C THOMAS, PUBLISHER

SPRINGFIELD · ILLINOIS BALTIMORE · MARYLAND

Published by CHARLES C THOMAS
220 EAST MONROE STREET, SPRINGFIELD, ILLINOIS

FIRST EDITION

Printed in the United States of America

PREFACE

THIS small handbook contains essentially the material covered in the Lectures on Physiology given in the School of Aviation Medicine, Naval Air Station, Pensacola, Florida. It was thought that it would be advantageous to publish these lectures as an aid to the students in this school and in similar schools. It is hoped that the material will also be of interest to aviators who realize that it is just as important to study the man in the plane as it is to know the characteristics of the plane. The opinions and assertions contained therein are the private ones of the writer and are not to be construed as official or reflecting the views of the Navy Department.

Lieutenant Frederick B. Lee, USNR, kindly consented to write a chapter on Instrument Flight and the author wishes to thank him for this chapter. The author also wishes to thank Captain F. Ceres, MC, USN, and Commander Rex White, MC, USN, for their many helpful suggestions in the preparation of this short text.

December 19, 1942

CHALMERS L. GEMMILL
School of Aviation Medicine
Naval Air Station
Pensacola, Florida

PHYSIOLOGY IN AVIATION

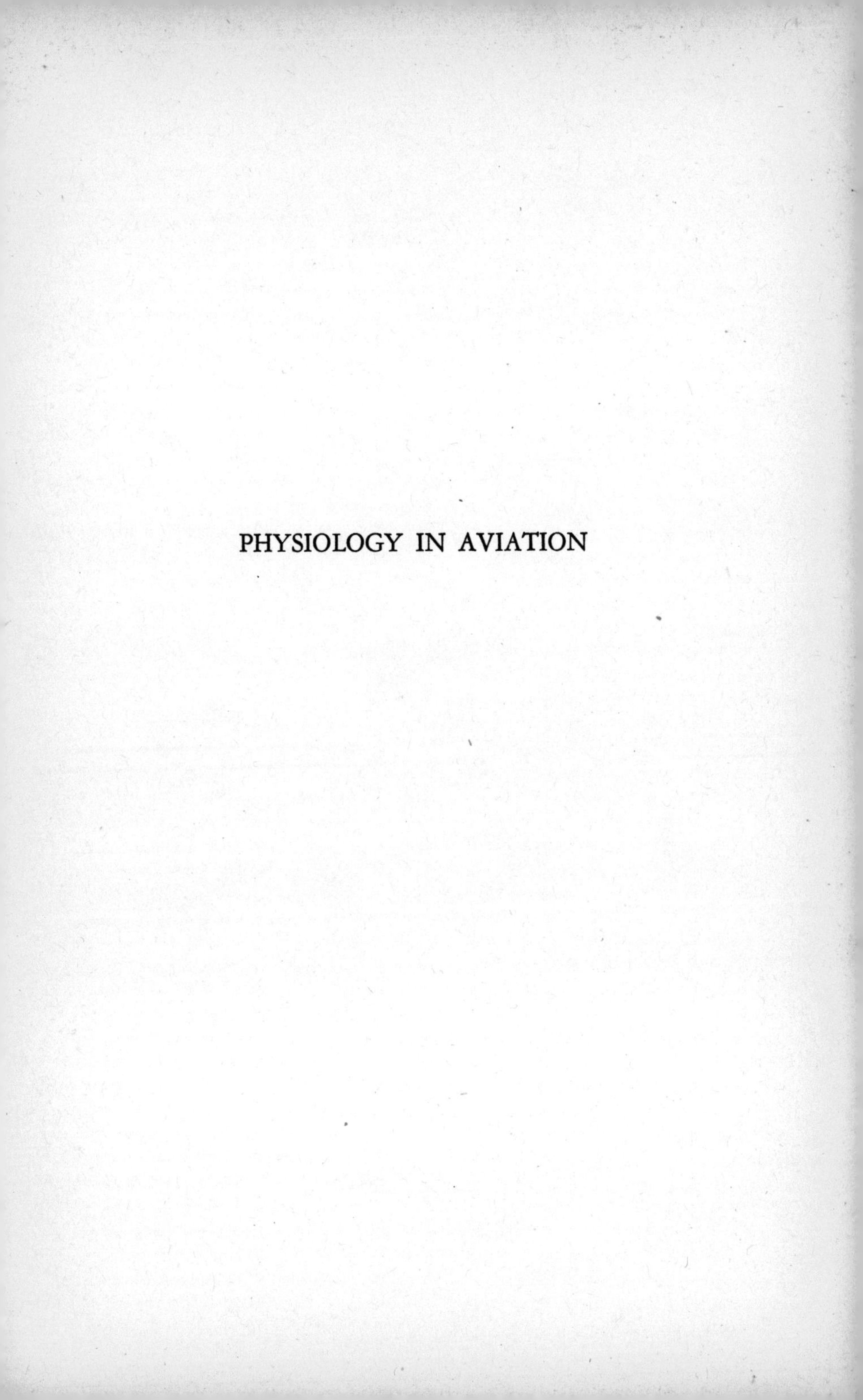

PHYSIOLOGY IN AVIATION

Chapter I

PHYSIOLOGY APPLIED TO AVIATION

The content of Physiology was formerly a study of organs and their functions. The newer teaching, however, treats the body as a unit and determines how the body reacts to external stimuli in order that the internal environment of the body may meet these new conditions in the external world. This approach has made Physiology of great value to Aviation.

In this field normal subjects, selected by careful physical and mental examinations, are subjected to anoxia, acceleration, mental and physical fatigue, vibration, fear, cold, toxic gases and, in war, to enemy action. Some of these changes in the aviator's external environment are greater than man has experienced before in his existence. For example, in high altitude flying to 40,000 feet, the aviator is subjected to a temperature of —55°C. and to a barometric pressure of 140.7 mm. Hg. Occasionally, on the surface of the earth, man has experienced this extreme cold but only such a decrease in barometric pressure under experimental conditions.

Another example of these changes in external environment never before encountered by man are the accelerations in aviation. These changes in his external environment must be met by corresponding changes in the man's internal environment in order that the aviator may accomplish his military mission. *That is the first purpose of military flying, the actual flying of the plane is secondary.* Therefore, the flyer must be given every physiological aid to enable him to accomplish his mission with a minimum amount of physical and of mental discomfort. In order to do this, the reactions of the human body to acceleration, change in pressure and other factors in aviation must be thoroughly understood that these marked changes in his external environment may be met by the aviator.

Physiological Selection of Aviators: It is obvious that men selected for aviation training must be physiologically normal. For that reason, the cadet's eyesight must be perfect, color vision normal, sense of equilibrium good and heart and lungs anatomically and physiologically sound. Therefore, every part of the original physical examination is based on the selection of a physiologically normal individual and the physical standards set by the Army and Navy must be adhered to in the selection of cadets.

With the modern development of the plane, another set of standards is met, for aviators must be able to tolerate the cold of high altitudes and to have a good resistance to anoxia and to aeroembolism. Therefore, physiological selection and classification of aviators are necessary in order to place the proper men in these planes. This physiological selection proceeds all through the training of the cadet from the moment he steps before the examining board until he receives his wings and is sent to a specialized squadron. In his squadron, selection ends but training continues. Therefore, the more accurately the Flight Surgeon understands the stresses and strains placed on the man, the more careful will be his original examination of candidates for aviation training, and the more interest will be taken in the classification, training and maintenance of the aviator.

It is the purpose of this book to give the physiological background of the changes produced in the body of man during flying, so that the Flight Surgeon may understand the physiological reaction of man in flight.

CHAPTER II

HISTORICAL INTRODUCTION

Man has long desired to fly. The Ancients observed the easy flight of birds and pictured themselves with wings flying from place to place with motive power derived from their leg or arm muscles. Angels and cherubs were endowed with this ability. There are many references in the Bible to this special power of man, especially as an aid for his ascent to heaven. Even these early imaginary flights were not without accidents. For example, there is the well-known story of *Daedalus* and *Icarus* in mythology. *Icarus* flew too close to the sun, melting the wax fastening his wings to his body. His wings fell off and Icarus spun into the sea (Figure 1).

In these early accounts of flying, man flew by the power transmitted to moving wings by his arm muscles. One of the earliest attempts to make a scientific analysis of animal flight and to put this study to practical use was that of *da Vinci* (1452-1519) in his study of the stability and the control of flight in birds. In his writings are designs of machines with wings. These were propelled by man with the intent to copy the flight of birds. Whether or not da Vinci ever put his ideas to practical test is not known. *Borelli,* the great Italian physiologist, in 1663, computed the force necessary to lift the body of a man from the ground and concluded that it was impossible for man to fly by his own motive power. His calculations put a temporary end to man's plans to fly in the same manner as a bird although, even today, there are discussions of the possibility of man flying by his own muscular energy. However, there is no more reason for man to fly by means of moving wing surfaces than there is for him to propel his ships by fish-like movements.

The next development came at the end of the eighteenth century. Many men, at that time, were interested in gases.

FIGURE 1
The Flight of Daedalus and the Fall of Icarus.
Taken from an old wood cut.

Carbon dioxide, oxygen, hydrogen, and nitrogen were recognized as pure gases and their properties were thoroughly investigated. This interest in gas led *Charles,* a French chemist, to construct balloons and to study their carrying capacity. The next step was the construction of a balloon large enough to carry man away from his natural domain, the earth. This was done by the two *Montgolfier* brothers, using heated air in their balloon. They ascended from a field near Paris in 1783. This balloon ascension stimulated many flights and

FIGURE 2

An Imaginary Balloon. Taken from Robertson, La Minerve, Paris, 1820.

considerable development in this field. *Blanchard* and *Jeffrey* flew the English Channel in 1785. Many other notable flights and parachute jumps were made in these early days. The idea of aerial travel again occupied the minds of men and much thought was given to the use of the balloon in peace and war. One of the more elaborate designs in this field is shown in Figure 2. In this imaginary balloon, there is room for a church, smaller balloons, armed guards, cannon and even a sail for steering. The latter idea illustrates the weakness of

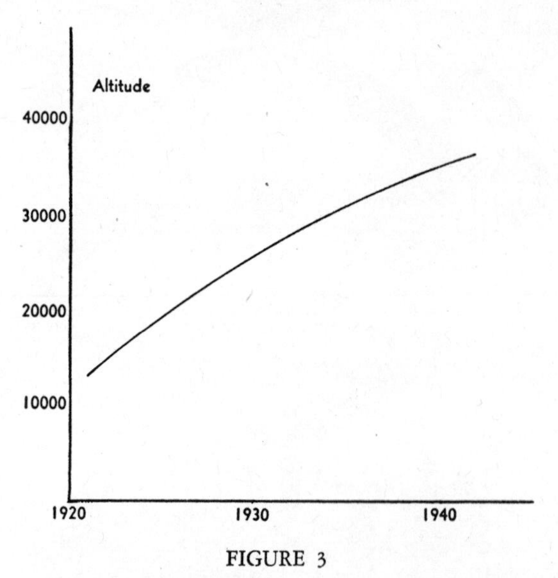

FIGURE 3
Altitude records made by standard service planes from 1920 to 1940.

the balloon for it must go with the winds. Not until the development of the gasoline engine was the balloon made useful. The most remarkable of these lighter-than-air craft were the *Zeppelins,* designed to carry crew, passengers and freight around the globe.

The development of heavier-than-air machines came much later than the lighter-than-air. *Langley* experimented with several models and made an almost successful flight in 1903. His machine, however, crashed into the Potomac River and his experiments failed. It was the *Wright* brothers who first conquered the air by their flight on December 17, 1903. From this development grew the present day flying in

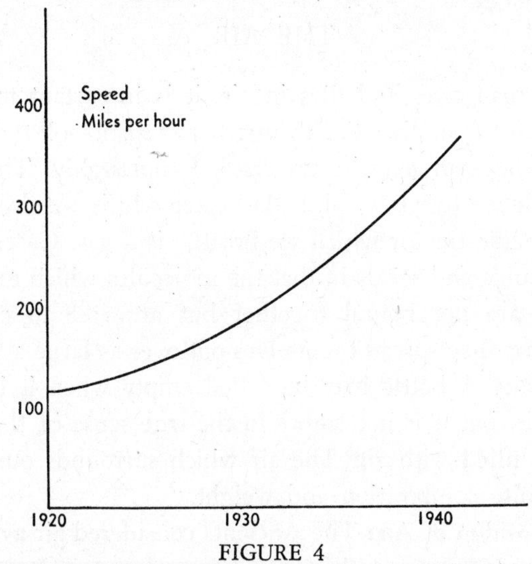

FIGURE 4
Speed records made by standard service planes from 1920 to 1940.

aeroplanes. A glance at the charts in Figures 3 and 4 will give an idea of the rapid progress in this field. Therefore, in the lifetime of many individuals living today, the amazing advancement of this field occurred.

CHAPTER III

THE AIR

Since man lives and flies in air, it is important to study this ocean of air that the flying characteristics of the plane and of the man may be understood thoroughly. The land on which we live is a solid, the water which we drink is a liquid, while the air which we breathe is a gas. Gases differ from liquids and solids in that the molecules which make up the gas are not bound together but are free to expand. Therefore, they spread themselves out over as large a volume as possible. A bottle may be called empty when it is open to the air, but it is not empty in the true sense of the word for it is filled with air. The air which surrounds our globe has definite composition and weight.

Composition of Air: The Ancients considered air as one of the elements along with earth, fire and water. It was not until the end of the eighteenth century that air was recognized as being composed of many elements. Modern analyses have demonstrated that air has the composition shown in Table 1, next page.

It may be noticed in the table that nitrogen is the most prevalent gas in the air while oxygen occupies only about one-fifth of the total volume. The rare gases occupy such a small proportional part that their amounts are generally added to that of nitrogen and the sum, 79.04 per cent, is called "nitrogen." However, *it must be kept in mind that one per cent of that "nitrogen" is composed of the rare gases.*

This composition is constant. If analyses are made on air from any part of the globe, it is found that there are not significant variations from the values given in Table 1. The reason for this is that the animal and vegetable kingdom are in equilibrium. The animal takes in oxygen and gives off carbon dioxide, the plant takes in carbon dioxide and gives

TABLE 1

COMPOSITION OF AIR

Element	*Symbol*	*Per cent*
Oxygen	O_2	20.93
Carbon Dioxide	CO_2	0.03
Nitrogen	N_2	78.08
Argon	A	0.94
Neon	Ne	0.0018
Hydrogen	H_2	0.0010
Helium	He	0.0005
Krypton	Kr	Trace
Xenon	Xe	Trace

off oxygen. These two processes are balanced in such a manner that *the composition of the air is constant.*

The same constant composition is found as flights are made into high altitudes. The composition of the air, for example, at 40,000 feet is the same as at sea level. In fact, the composition of oxygen only begins to decrease when heights of 80,000 feet are reached. Above this height, the oxygen and nitrogen contents decrease while the amounts of hydrogen and helium increase. It is speculated that the composition of the atmosphere is such that altitudes of over sixty miles must be reached before the oxygen content falls to a trace (Figure 5). At the present time flights have been made to 47,000 feet with man in an open cockpit plane, to 56,000 feet in a pressure suit and to 72,000 feet in a stratosphere balloon. The air surrounding these planes and the balloon had the same composition by volume as sea-level air. It is well-known that man suffers from the effects of the lack of oxygen at high altitudes. Since it is not the percentage composition of the air, there must be

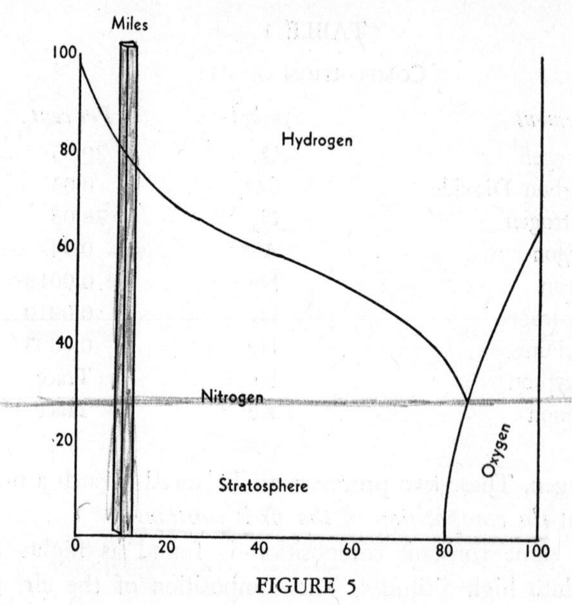

FIGURE 5

Percentage of gases in atmospheric air at various altitudes. Abscissa, per cent; ordinate, miles.

another factor which changes with altitude. That factor is the *barometric pressure.*

Barometric Pressure: If a pipe of one square inch cross sectional diameter could be shoved through the atmosphere (Figure 5), and if the air in this pipe could be collected and weighed, the collected air would weigh 14.7 pounds. Therefore, the weight of the column of air pressing on every square inch of our bodies is 14.7 pounds. This is one method of expressing air or barometric pressure.

Another method of recording pressure is in the number of millimeters of mercury which will be supported by the column of air above the surface of the earth. At sea level, this column of air will support 760 mm. of mercury (29.92 inches), while at 18,000 feet one-half of the air is below

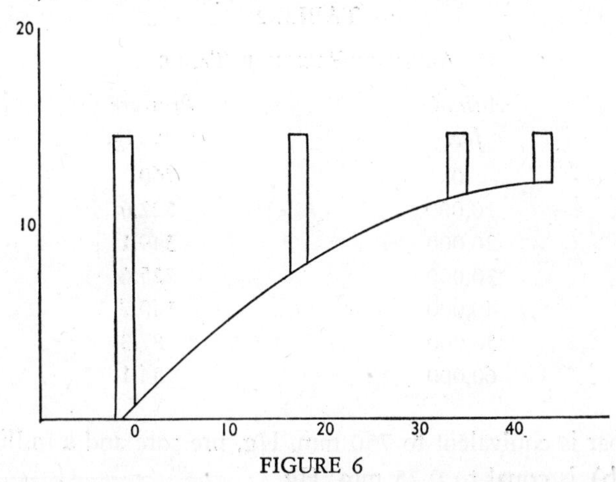

FIGURE 6

Weights of columns of air at various altitudes. Abscissa, altitude in thousands of feet; ordinate, weight of air in pounds per square inch. This graph shows that at 18,000 feet, one-half of the weight of the air is below, one-half above; at 42,000 feet, one-sixth of the weight of the air is above, five-sixths is below.

and one-half above an observer at this altitude. Therefore, at 18,000 feet, the mercury column will only be supported to a height of 380 mm., one-half of that at sea level. At 34,000 feet it would be at 190 mm. or one-fourth of the sea level value (Figure 6). The relationship between altitude in feet and mm. mercury pressure is given in Table 2. The greater part of the atmosphere over us is close to the surface of the earth. Therefore, the greater changes in atmospheric pressure occur during ascents through a distance close to the earth's surface than through air at an equivalent distance higher from the ground. This change of pressure modifies the reaction of man and the performance of a plane at higher altitudes (Chapter X). Another method of expressing barometric pressure is in terms of a bar (b).

TABLE 2

ALTITUDE-PRESSURE TABLE

Altitude feet	*Pressure mm. Hg.*
0	760
10,000	522.6
20,000	349.1
30,000	225.6
40,000	140.7
50,000	87.3
60,000	54.1

A bar is equivalent to 750 mm. Hg. pressure and a millibar (mb) is equal to 0.75 mm. Hg.

Temperature: The temperature drops approximately 1°C. with every 500 feet of increase in altitude until altitudes of 35,000 feet are reached. At this altitude the temperature is −55°C. (−67°F.) (Fig. 7). The temperature remains constant as further increases in altitude are gained. Therefore, *there are two chief zones of temperature around the earth;* (1) the troposphere or region of changing temperature and the (2) stratosphere or region of constant (isothermal) temperature.

This exteme cold affects the reaction of man at high altitude just as much as the decrease in barometric pressure. Therefore, a chapter (Chapter XVII) is given to the discussion of the methods used by man to combat this external cold as well as methods used to combat the fall in barometric pressure associated with altitude.

Density Altitude: The flight engineer compares the performance of his plane at any altitude to the density of the air at that altitude, while the flight surgeon thinks in terms of pressure altitude on the man. These two methods of

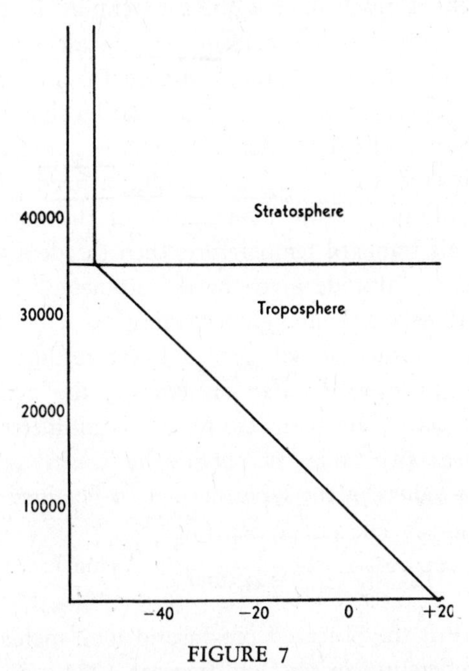

FIGURE 7
The effect of altitude on temperature. Abscissa, temperature in degrees Centigrade; ordinate, altitude in feet.

determining altitude may give different results and, therefore, *any statement regarding altitude must be qualified by the method of obtaining that altitude.*

An altimeter gives the number of feet that the plane is above the surface of the sea. This is obtained by calibrating the instrument in terms of feet for a given pressure in mm.

of mercury. In order to make this calibration, the temperature of the air column must be known. Certain assumptions about the temperature of the air are made in the calibration. It is assumed that the temperature falls lineally until the stratosphere is reached, that the temperature in the stratosphere is −55°C. (−67°F.) and that the air is dry. If, at a given altitude, the temperature is different from those values, then the density or weight of a standard volume of air at that altitude would be different. Therefore, the calibration of an altimeter is based upon assuming a fixed temperature for each altitude. If the temperature of the outside air is equal to this standard temperature, then the density altitude will equal the altitude given by the altimeter. If the air is warmer, it will give a higher reading on a density basis; if the air is cooler, it will give a lower reading.

Therefore, *to obtain density altitude,* the aviator must know the actual air temperature at his altimeter altitude. Having these two values, he obtains the density ratio from a table. The values in the table have been obtained from the equation

$$\text{Density ratio} = 0.3789 \times \frac{P(\text{mm})}{T(\text{C}^\circ \text{Abs})}$$

in which P is the observed pressure in mm. mercury and T is the temperature in absolute degrees (273° + observed temperature in ° C.). Having obtained the density ratio, the density altitude may be obtained by consulting a table (Table 3).

For example, if an altimeter records 30,000 feet and the outside temperature is −44.4°C., the density ratio is 0.3740 and the density altitude is 30,000 feet. However, if the temperature is −40.0°C., then the density ratio is

$$\text{Density ratio} = 0.3789 \times \frac{225.6}{273 + 40} = 0.2731$$

and this density ratio (0.2731) compares to an altitude of 35,000 feet. All high altitude records are made in terms of density altitude. The exact pressure altitude which affects the

TABLE 3

Altitude feet	*Pressure mm. Hg.*	*Temperature °C*	*Density Ratio*
0	760	15.0	1.000
10,000	522.6	−4.8	0.7384
20,000	349.1	−24.6	0.5327
30,000	225.6	−44.4	0.3740
40,000	140.7	−55.0	0.2447

performance of man may be much less or greater than this density altitude depending on the actual external temperature.

Summary: **A study of the composition, pressure and temperature of the air which man breathes and in which he flies is given. It is important to remember that altitudes may be expressed in terms of density altitude or pressure altitude. Since it is the change in barometric pressure which affects the reaction of man at high altitudes,** ***all altitudes in this book will be pressure altitudes.***

CHAPTER IV

THE GAS LAWS AND THEIR APPLICATION TO AVIATION MEDICINE

In order to evaluate the problems associated with the gases involved in respiration and their changes which occur in altitude flying, it is necessary to know and to understand the gas laws. *These laws are designed for ideal gases, gases which do not exist in nature.* However, when applied to respiratory gases, they are sufficiently accurate to give reliable results without further correction. The names of their discoverers have been given to these laws. This is confusing for it is difficult to remember the exact relationship in connection with a name. Therefore, these relationships will be presented in terms of the variables involved as well as the name of the discoverer.

The Relationship of Pressure to Volume (Boyle's Law): *Boyle* discovered in the seventeenth century that there was an inverse relationship between pressure and volume; if the pressure increases, the volume decreases. For example, if 12 liters of gas at one atmosphere of pressure was subjected to two atmospheres, the resulting volume would be six liters (Table 4).

TABLE 4

Pressure (p)	1	2	3	4	6
Volume (v)	12	6	4	3	2
	—	—	—	—	—
$p \times v$	12	12	12	12	12

Increasing the pressure still more, the volume gives a corresponding decrease. It is obvious from Table 4 that the product of any volume by its corresponding pressure gives the same number. Therefore, the product of one volume by its pressure must equal the product of a new volume by its new pressure, or

$$pv = p_1v_1.$$

This law finds many applications in respiration and aviation medicine. For example: if 100 liters of air are collected at 750 mm. pressure, what would this volume be at (1) 760 mm., (2) 446.4 mm. (14,000 feet) and at (3) 225.6 mm. (30,000 feet)?

$$pv = p_1v_1$$

(1) $750 \times 100 = 760 \times v_1$ $v_1 = 98.7$ liters
(2) $750 \times 100 = 446.4 \times v_1$ $v_1 = 168.3$ liters
(3) $750 \times 100 = 225.6 \times v_1$ $v_1 = 336.9$ liters

It is obvious that the volume of a gas will increase with altitude. Another practical application of this law is in the calculation of expansion of gases in the intestinal tract of an aviator ascending to a high altitude (Table 5).

TABLE 5

COMPARATIVE VOLUMES OF GAS AT VARIOUS ALTITUDES

Altitude feet	*Barometric Pressure mm. Hg.*	*Relative Gas volume*
0	760	1.00
17,962	380	2.00
33,705	190	4.00
38,389	152	5.00
42,151	127	6.00

Therefore, if an ascent to 38,389 feet, one volume of gas originally in the intestinal tract at sea level now occupies 5 volumes. This expansion of gas causes distention and abdominal discomfort in the aviator ascending to such altitudes, and may cause respiratory and circulatory distress if the expansion of the gas forces the diaphragm to push up on the heart and lungs.

The Relationship of Volume to Temperature (Charles' Law): The volume of a gas varies directly with the absolute temperature. This law gives the new volume of a gas when the temperature varies. It is expressed by the formula

$$\frac{V}{T} = \frac{V_1}{T_1}$$

in which V is the original volume, T the original temperature, V_1 the new volume and T_1 the new temperature.

Absolute temperature is obtained by adding 273°C. to the temperature in degrees centigrade. An easier method of using this relationship is to employ a coefficient of expansion. For air, this factor is 0.003665. This figure signifies that one liter of air will expand 0.003665 liters per degree centigrade change in temperature. Therefore, it is only necessary to multiply the temperature change in degrees by this factor in order to get the change in volume of the gas. If this change is added to the old volume, the new volume is obtained. The complete formula for using the coefficient of expansion is

$$V_1 = V_0(1 + 0.003665t)$$

in which V is the new volume, V_0 the original volume, and t, the temperature change in degrees Centigrade. It is to be noted that in this formula temperature is used in degrees centigrade, while in the preceding formula temperature is given in absolute units.

This formula aids in the calculation of the change of volume of gases with temperature. In respiration all gases must be reduced to standard conditions, 760 mm. pressure and 0°C. temperature for comparative purposes. The supply of oxygen at high altitudes will be conditioned by temperature changes. An example of the application of this law to respiratory studies is as follows: A spirometer contains 100 liters of air in a room at 20°C. If the temperature of the room should change to 30°C., what would be the resulting change in volume of the spirometer?

Solution 1.

$$\frac{V}{T} = \frac{V^1}{T^1}$$

$$\frac{100}{273 + 20} = \frac{V^1}{273 + 30}$$

$$\frac{100}{293} = \frac{V^1}{303}$$

$$V^1 = 103.4 \text{ liters.}$$

Solution 2.

$$V^1 = V_o\ (1 + 0.003665t)$$
$$V^1 = 100\ (1 + 0.003665t)$$
$$V^1 = 100\ (1.03665)$$
$$V^1 = 103.6 \text{ liters.}$$

The two solutions do not give identical results since solution 1 is applicable only in the case of ideal gases.

The Law of Partial Pressures: This is one of the most commonly used laws in respiration and in aviation medicine. It states that the total pressure of a gas mixture is made up of the sum of the partial pressures of the individual gases. The following examples illustrate the use of this law in the calculation of the partial pressures of gases in atmospheric air. The percentages of these gases have been given as 20.93 per cent for oxygen, 0.03 per cent for carbon dioxide and 79.06 per cent for nitrogen. Therefore, oxygen will exert 20.93 per cent of the total pressure.

At sea level, the calculations will be:—

Oxygen	$20.93 \times 760 =$	159.07 mm. Hg.
Carbon Dioxide	$0.03 \times 760 =$	.23 mm. Hg.
Nitrogen	$79.04 \times 760 =$	600.70 mm. Hg.
	Sum =	760.00 mm. Hg.

At 20,000 feet, where the barometric pressure is 349.2 mm. the pressure exerted by each gas is:

Oxygen	$20.93 \times 349.2 =$	73.1
Carbon dioxide	$0.03 \times 349.2 =$	.1
Nitrogen	$79.06 \times 349.2 =$	276.0
	Sum =	349.2

It is obvious that with increasing altitudes, the partial pressure of oxygen will fall in alveolar air. However, in this case, there is another factor which must be taken into consideration: *the pressure of water vapor.* This pressure is a constant, 47 mm. of Hg., and is not changed by variations in atmospheric pressure. If the analysis of alveolar air gave 15.00 per cent oxygen, 5.00 per cent for carbon dioxide and 80.00 per cent for nitrogen, the tensions of the three gases are calculated as follows:

		mm. Hg.
Total tension		760
Tension of water vapor		47
Available for respiratory gases		713
For oxygen	$15.00 \times 713 =$	106.95
For carbon dioxide	$5.00 \times 713 =$	35.65
For nitrogen	$80.00 \times 713 =$	570.40
		713.00
In water vapor		47.00
	Total	760.00

Since water vapor occupies 47 mm. of the total tension, there is available for the respiratory gases only 713 of the total tension available for the three gases: oxygen, carbon dioxide and nitrogen. Although at sea level the tension of water vapor is small in comparison with the total, at high altitudes it may play a big rôle. For example, at 40,000 feet, the total barometric tension is 140.7 mm. In this case, water vapor would occupy 47/140.7 or 33 per cent of the total available tension. At 63,000 feet, the atmospheric pressure is 46.9 mm. At this altitude, the space in the lungs would be completely occupied by water vapor and there would be no room for respiratory gases.

Law of Diffusion of Gases (Graham's Law): The law deals with relative speeds of diffusion of gases. The relative speed of diffusion of gases is inversely proportional to the square roots of their relative densities. Taking hydrogen as 1, the relative speeds of diffusion of other gases to hydrogen or to any other gas may be calculated by this law (Table 6).

TABLE 6

RELATIVE DIFFUSION OF GASES

Gas	*Relative density*	*Calculated speed of diffusion*	*Measured speed of diffusion*
Hydrogen	1	1	1
Helium	4	0.5	—
Methane	8	0.354	0.351
CO	14	0.267	0.278
N_2	14	0.267	0.265
O_2	16	0.250	0.248
CO_2	22	0.213	0.212

An example of the use of this law in the substitution of helium for nitrogen during diving operations or in the treatment of asthma. Helium will diffuse faster than nitrogen on account of the fact that helium is the lighter gas. The relative rates of diffusion of these two gases would be $\frac{\sqrt{14}}{\sqrt{4}}$ or $\frac{3.8}{2}$ which equals 1.9. Therefore, helium will diffuse almost twice as fast as nitrogen through the trachea and bronchi into the lungs as nitrogen.

Law of Solution of Gases: The law involves the amounts of gas which go into solution. When a mixture of gases is exposed to a liquid, the amount of each gas which is dissolved in the liquid is proportional to the partial pressure of the gas. The amounts of gas which will go into solution have been experimentally determined and are given in terms of absorption coefficients. This coefficient gives the amount of gas in cc. which will be dissolved in 1 cc. of a liquid per 1 atmosphere of the gas. The absorption coefficient varies with the type of gas and liquid, the temperature and presence of salts or proteins in the liquid. The absorption coefficients for blood at 37.0°C. for the three respiratory gases are given in Table 7.

TABLE 7

ABSORPTION COEFFICIENTS FOR BLOOD AT 37.0°

Oxygen	0.019
Carbon dioxide	0.510
Nitrogen	0.00954

Taking the tensions obtained in the problem given above for alveolar air, it is an easy matter to calculate the amount of gas carried in physical solution by the blood in this case.

For oxygen: $0.019 : 760 = X : 106.95$
$X = .00268$

For carbon dioxide: $0.510 : 760 = X : 35.65$
$X = .0239$

For nitrogen: $.00954 : 760 = X : 570.40$
$X = .00722$

These examples give the amounts of gases carried in physical solution in the blood under ordinary conditions. For example, in 100 cc. of blood, 0.268 cc. of oxygen, 2.39 cc. of carbon dioxide and 0.722 cc. of nitrogen are carried in physical solution.

Summary: In this chapter the gas laws are discussed. In later chapters, these laws will be used to illustrate the differences between the physical and chemical carriage of gases in the blood, in the explanation of aeroembolism, in the use of oxygen at high altitudes and in many other examples.

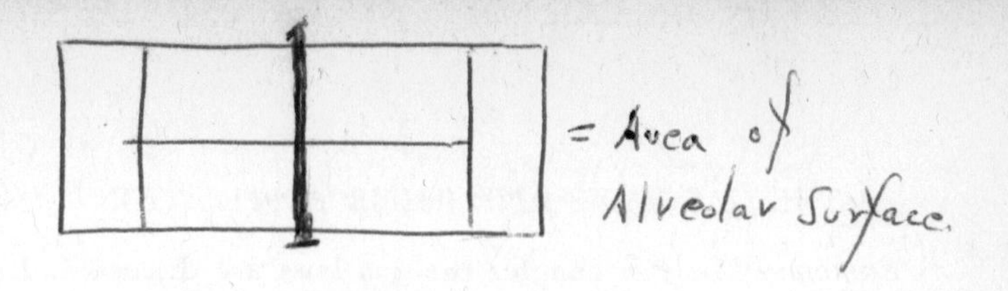

CHAPTER V

MECHANICS OF RESPIRATION

In order that atmospheric air may reach the alveoli, certain coordinated respiratory movements must take place. These movements are divided into inspiration and expiration. However, before a detailed description of these movements may be given, it is necessary to review the anatomy of the lungs.

Anatomy of the Lungs: Following the subdivision of the trachea into bronchi and the bronchi into the bronchioles, there is further subdivision. The finer bronchioles, the respiratory bronchioles, are subdivided into alveolar ducts, five or six coming from each bronchiole. Each alveolar duct gives rise to 3 to 6 alveolar sacs, which dilate into alveoli. There is a rich network of capillaries around each alveoli. In some regions, there is a layer of pulmonary epithelium and capillary endothelium between the air in the alveoli and the blood in the capillary. In other regions, the pulmonary epithelium is deficient and there is only the thin layer of capillary endothelium between the alveolar air and the blood in the capillaries. The subdivision of the lung spaces makes for a large surface for interchange of gases. It is said that the alveolar surface is so large that if all the alveoli were spread out flat, they would cover an area equal to a tennis court.

Inspiration: In inspiration, the thoracic cage is enlarged in all of its dimensions; vertical, transverse and anterior-posterior. The enlargement is not equal in all of these dimensions but varies due to the anatomical arrangement of the ribs and sternum and with the type of respiration. The

?

movements of the ribs will be considered from above downward. The elevation of the first pair of ribs and the manubrium of the sternum increases the anterior-posterior diameter of the thorax, thus expanding this portion for the apices of the lungs. The elevation of the 2nd to the 6th pair of ribs also increases the anterior-posterior diameter of the thorax, and, in addition, enlarges the transverse diameter of the thorax. The swinging outward of the 7th to the 10th pairs

TABLE 8

TABLE FOR RESPIRATORY MOVEMENTS

INSPIRATION

Ribs (pairs)	*Anterior-posterior diameter* A-P	*Transverse diameter* T
1st	+	0
2–6	+	+
7–10	—	+
10–12	0	0

+, increase in size; —, decrease in size; 0, no change in size.

of ribs widens the transverse diameter with a slight reduction of the anterior-posterior diameter. The 11th and 12th (floating) ribs play very little rôle in respiration. Their muscular attachments may act with the abdominal muscles as antagonists to the diaphragm, relaxing when the diaphragm descends, contracting during ascent. These changes are summarized in Table 8.

Expiration: Expiration is a passive act *during quiet breathing*. The lungs contract due to their own elasticity and the thorax returns to its inspiratory size. *In forced expiration,* the size of the thoracic cavity is reduced by the active contraction of the abdominal muscles, by the ascent of the diaphragm and by active depression of the ribs from contraction of internal intercostal muscles.

Action of the Diaphragm: The total surface of this muscle may be considered to be between 270 and 300 cc. It descends under normal conditions of breathing about 1.2 cm., while during forced breathing it may descend as much as 3 cms. This means that a descent of the diaphragm of 1.2 cm. will enlarge the thoracic cavity 360 cc. during quiet breathing while during forced breathing, it may enlarge this cavity 900 cc. The greater part of the change in the thoracic contents may be produced by movements of the diaphragm during quiet breathing.

Intrapulmonic Pressures: Since the trachea, bronchi and alveoli are open to the external air, the pressure in these regions is equal to atmospheric pressure at the end of inspiration and expiration. However, during inspiration, pressure will fall, while on expiration, it will rise. This is due to the fact that it takes a short interval to equalize the pressure in the air spaces of the lungs with the atmospheric pressure. The magnitude of these pressure changes depends on the rapidity of breathing and on the condition of the respiratory tract. For example, if forced expiration is attempted with the glottis closed, large changes in pressure may result. In quiet inspiration the fall of intrapulmonic pressure equals 9 to 10 mm. of water but by closing the glottis and producing a forced expiration, this pressure may be increased to 100 mm. of mercury. During a forced inspiration with the glottis closed, this pressure may be lowered to −80 mm. of mercury. The Royal Air Force has used these changes as a test of respiratory control. The subject is told to raise a column of mercury 40 mm. high, and to hold it at this height as long as he is able. The test gives a rough indication of the strength of respiratory muscles and of respiratory control.

Intrathoracic Pressures: On account of the elastic pull of the lungs, there is a negative pressure between the layer of pleura. The negative pressure at the end of inspiration is about −4.5 mm. of Hg., while at the end of expiration it is about −7.5 mm. of Hg. If the thoracic cage is punctured, the lungs will collapse.

Subdivision of Air in Lungs: There are two general methods for subdivision of air in the lungs. The first method is to subdivide the air in the lungs according to the vital capacity and residual air.

Vital capacity is the air breathed out from maximal inspiration to maximal expiration. The vital capacity is related to the body surface. Vital capacity in liters divided by surface area of the body in meters should give a value of 2.5 for a normal individual. Therefore, if a man's vital capacity is 5.0 liters and his surface area is 1.9 square meters, his ratio would be $\frac{5.0}{1.9}$ or 2.6. This man's vital capacity is 4 per cent over the normal value for this ratio. Vital capacity is very much decreased under some conditions such as uncompensated myocardial insufficiency.

Vital capacity, in turn, is subdivided into *tidal air, complemental air* and *supplemental air.*

Tidal air is the air breathed in and out with each normal respiration.

Complemental air is the air breathed in from normal respiration to maximal inspiration.

Supplemental air is the air breathed out from normal expiration to maximal expiration.

Residual air is the air remaining in the lungs after maximal expiration. No matter how hard an expiration is produced, there will always be some air remaining in the lungs.

***Summary:* In this chapter the mechanics of respiration are discussed and a method of subdividing the air in the lungs is given. A knowledge of intrapulmonic pressure is necessary for the Flight Surgeon's understanding of the working of the Demand Type of Oxygen Equipment.**

Chapter VI

ALVEOLAR AIR

Since the air in the alveoli is in active interchange with the gases in the blood, the body is not in equilibrium with atmospheric air but with *alveolar air.* Therefore, a thorough knowledge of alveolar air is necessary for our understanding of the transport of gases by the blood (Chapters VII and VIII). The alveolar air is in contrast to the air in the trachea, bronchi and bronchioles. In these regions, there is no interchange of gas with the blood and, therefore, this air is said to be in the *dead spaces.* The air in the dead spaces is very small in volume in comparison to the air in the alveoli since the dead space air only occupies about 200 cc.

Alveolar air may be determined by expiring through a long tube with a forced expiration. This causes the air in the dead space to be blown out through the tube and moves the alveolar air into the tube. By quickly taking a sample at the side tube alveolar air may be obtained and this sample analyzed for its carbon dioxide, oxygen and nitrogen content. The percentages obtained are converted into *tensions. The amount of tension* gives the driving force for the interchange of the gas in the alveolar air with the blood and between the blood and tissues. There are four components, oxygen, carbon dioxide, nitrogen, and water vapor, which must be considered in calculating tensions from percentages. Water vapor is a constant at all altitudes and under all pressures. It is 47 mm. of Hg. at body temperature. Therefore, there are only 760—47 or 713 mm. Hg. remaining for the oxygen, carbon dioxide and nitrogen. An example of the calculation of the tension of alveolar air at sea level, is given in the following table (Table 9).

It is to be noted that the tension of water vapor does not change with altitude. This value is given as 47 mm. Hg. at body temperature. At sea level, 47 mm. of the total pressure, 760, is only a small fraction. At high altitudes, however, it becomes of increasing importance. For example, at 34,000 feet the water vapor now exerts 43/190 or 33% of the total pressure. It is obvious that this pressure exerted

TABLE 9

CALCULATION OF ALVEOLAR AIR TENSIONS

Analyses of alveolar air gave for O_2, 15.5%; for CO_2, 4.5%; and N_2, 80%.

Sea Level

	$760 - 47$	$= 713$
CO_2	$713 \times .0450$	$= 32.09$ mm.
O_2	713×0.155	$= 110.51$ mm.
N_2	713×0.80	$= 570.40$ mm.

by water vapor becomes of increasing importance with altitude and is one of the limiting factors in high altitude flying.

Factors Influencing Composition of Alveolar Air: The many factors which influence the composition of alveolar air are taken up in order of their importance.

In the first place, alveolar air composition taken under standard conditions is markedly constant. *Haldane* found that the carbon dioxide composition was 5.63 per cent with a deviation of only 0.2 per cent over a period of two years. There is a slight variation between a sample taken at the end of normal inspiration from that taken at the end of expiration. Haldane gives an average value of 5.54 per cent carbon dioxide at the end of inspiration and 5.72 per cent at the end of expiration. The reason for this difference is that alveolar air is slightly diluted with atmospheric air during inspiration, and increases its concentration of carbon dioxide during expiration. This small difference also demonstrates the buffering power of the alveolar air spaces. Normally, the carbon dioxide content of the blood would only swing through a small change of carbon dioxide tension with normal respiratory activity. This is adequate to rid the blood of sufficient carbon dioxide in order that it does not increase in arterial blood.

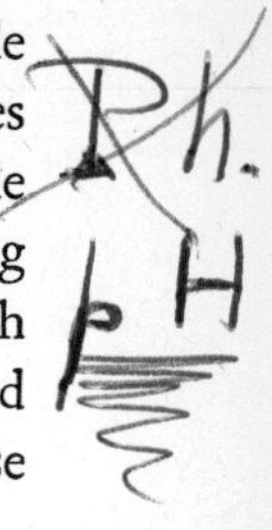

It was stated above that the changes in alveolar air carbon dioxide are very small with normal respiratory activity. However, if the ventilation is forced, or if the breath is held, there may be marked changes in the composition and tension of carbon dioxide. Forcing the ventilation will cause the carbon dioxide tension to fall, while holding the breath will cause the alveolar carbon dioxide to rise. However, if the rate of respiration is changed, allowing the depth to be controlled voluntarily, there is not a marked change in alveolar air percentage (Table 10).

TABLE 10

THE RELATIONSHIP OF RESPIRATORY RATE TO ALVEOLAR CARBON DIOXIDE

Respirations per minute	*Alveolar air CO_2 percentage*
30	5.62
4	5.66
3	5.71
60	6.16

The results in this table demonstrate that with a very fast rate of respiration, 60 per minute, the individual respirations are so shallow that there is not adequate ventilation.

Exercise does affect the alveolar air during moderate rates of working. The data given in Table 11 demonstrates that the rate of working increases the alveolar air concentration slightly. Ventilation was adequate to exhale sufficient carbon dioxide to keep the concentration in the body from increasing to abnormal values.

Barometric Pressure: Haldane observed the remarkable finding that the barometric pressure could be varied from sea level to 4640 mm. (6.1 atmospheres), without a change in the carbon dioxide percentage (Table 12). During de-

TABLE 11

RELATIONSHIP BETWEEN WORK AND CARBON DIOXIDE CONTENT OF ALVEOLAR AIR

	CO_2 per cent in alveolar air
Resting in bed	5.97
Walking 2 miles per hour	6.04
3 miles per hour	6.14
4 miles per hour	6.23
5 miles per hour	6.28

TABLE 12

RELATIONSHIP BETWEEN BAROMETRIC PRESSURE AND THE CARBON DIOXIDE CONTENT OF THE ALVEOLAR AIR

Atmospheric Pressure mm. Hg.	*Alveolar CO_2 percentage*	*Alveolar CO_2 mm. Hg.*
760	4.7	33.5
2310	1.8	40.7
3860	0.95	36.2
4640	0.75	34.4

creased barometric pressure, there is increase in carbon dioxide percentage, with the tension remaining constant. This continues until the individual starts to hyperventilate from the anoxia produced by the lowered barometric pressure. When this occurs, the tension of carbon dioxide falls.

The control of the respiratory center which maintains the carbon dioxide pressure constant is given up in favor of aiding the decreasing oxygen supply.

Fixed Acids: If fixed acids, such as lactic acid or β-hydroxybutyric acid, are produced, some of the base of the body will be matched against this fixed acid. Therefore, there will be less base to carry the carbon dioxide. The carbon dioxide tension in the blood and alveolar air will fall under these conditions.

Equilibrium of Alveolar Air With Arterial Blood: All modern experimental work has shown that the equilibrium between alveolar air and arterial blood is within two or three mm. of pressure, and that gases are transferred by physical processes. When the venous blood enters the alveolar capillaries, it very quickly comes in equilibrium with the gas in the alveoli and, therefore, by the time that it leaves the alveolar capillary, the gases in the blood are practically of the same tension as in the alveoli.

Since passage of gases through the alveolar wall and capillary endothelium is a physical process, the pressure difference between venous blood and alveolar air is one of the controlling factors. If the pressure of oxygen, for example, is low in the alveolar air, less oxygen will pass into the blood. The rate of the blood flow must be adequate, for if too fast, the blood may pass through the lungs before it has time to become completely saturated or, if too slow, it will become saturated before it has left the alveolar capillaries. The latter method is an inefficient process.

The physical properties of the membrane are very important in this connection. The area of the alveolar surfaces is about 90 square meters. Not all of this area is used during normal breathing for a differential opening and closing of alveoli has been described. However, if there is any pathological change in the lungs, such as fluid formation, the diffusion of gases may be markedly decreased due to a change in permeability of the alveolar membranes.

Summary: **A knowledge of the alveolar air, its properties and composition is important for the blood is in equilibrium with this air and not the atmospheric air. This chapter discusses alveolar air, its composition and the various factors affecting this composition.**

CHAPTER VII

THE CARRIAGE OF OXYGEN BY THE BLOOD

The most important function of hemoglobin is to carry oxygen to the tissues from the lungs. This molecule is made up of two portions, the heme and the globin. The heme part of the molecule contains iron. The molecular weight of the molecule is 68,000 and contains 4 atoms of iron in the ferrous state. This iron does not change to the ferric state when the molecule combines with oxygen. In fact, the exact nature of the combination of oxygen with hemoglobin is not known. It exists in the red blood cells in amounts of 16 grams per 100 cc. of blood.

Oxygen-hemoglobin Dissociation Curve: Sixteen grams of hemoglobin are able to take up 21 cc. of oxygen when the hemoglobin is fully saturated with oxygen. This is almost eighty times the amount of oxygen dissolved in physical solution in the blood. However, the saturation of hemoglobin with oxygen and of plasma is dependent on the partial pressure of oxygen. The graphic relationship between the saturation of hemoglobin and the pressure of oxygen is called the oxygen-hemoglobin dissociation curve (Figure 8). This is a very important relationship and must be understood in order that the effects of reduction of barometric pressure may be made clear.

This curve is obtained by analysis of the oxygen content of blood and the oxygen content of air with which the blood is in equilibrium. In order to obtain this equilibrium, a measured amount of blood is placed in a tonometer, and air containing oxygen of a certain percentage is passed into the tonometer. The stopcocks are closed and the vessel is rotated in a water bath at body temperature. After equilibrium has been attained, both the blood and the gas are analyzed for their oxygen contents. For example, if the gas contains 10 per cent of oxygen and the blood has 8 cc. of oxygen in every 100 cc., the tension of oxygen is $(760 - 47) \times 0.10$

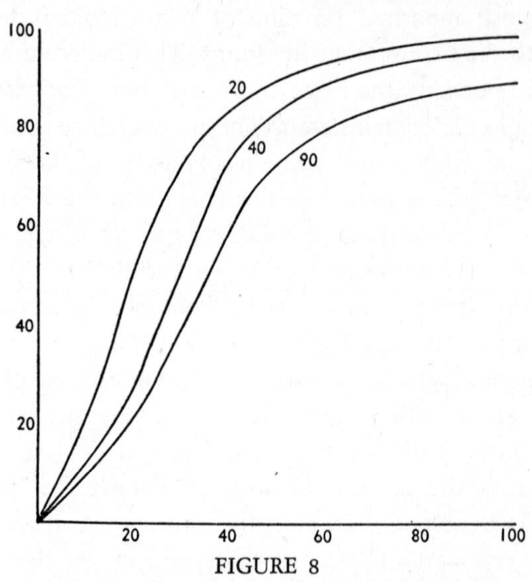

FIGURE 8

Oxygen-hemoglobin dissociation curves. Abscissa, tension of oxygen in mm. Hg. Curves are given for 20, 40, and 90 mm. of carbon dioxide tension.

or 71.3 mm. Hg. If this sample of blood is 100 per cent saturated when 21 cc. are present, then 8 cc. would represent 38 per cent saturation.

$$21 : 100 = 8 : x$$
$$x = 38 \text{ per cent}$$

By setting up a number of tubes containing the same amount of blood, but different amounts of oxygen, similar analysis will give a series of points. By joining these points with a smooth curve, the oxygen-hemoglobin dissociation curve is obtained.

Using this curve (Figure 8), it may be seen that when the tension in the alveoli is about 100 mm., the blood is 95 per cent saturated. To get 100 per cent saturation, it is necessary to increase the tension to 150 mm. Hg. Venous blood contains 15 cc. of oxygen in every 100 cc. of blood, for about 5 cc. are given up during the passage of 100 cc. of the blood through the capillaries. This means that the venous blood is 71 per cent saturated.

With the fall in barometric pressure at high altitudes, there is a fall in the oxygen tension in the lungs. With this fall in oxygen tension in the lungs, there is less driving force to get oxygen into the blood and therefore, the amount of oxygen present in the blood is less. For example, at 18,000 feet, the barometric pressure has fallen to 380 mm. of Hg. The tension of oxygen in the alveoli would fall from 100 to 50 mm. Hg. Therefore, the blood is only 70 per cent saturated at this altitude. Therefore, the amount of oxygen falls in the blood as well as the driving force to get oxygen into the tissues. These changes produce the signs and symptoms of anoxia.

Factors which Affect the Position of the Oxygen Hemoglobin Dissociation Curve: One of the chief factors which affects the position of this oxygen-hemoglobin dissociation curve is the tension of carbon dioxide in the blood (Figure 8). It can be seen in the figure that as the tension of carbon dioxide increases, the curve shifts towards the right. Therefore, for a given tension of oxygen, the blood will carry less oxygen when the carbon dioxide tension is raised. This shift in the position of the curve aids in the unloading of oxygen in the tissues (Figure 8). For example, when the tension of oxygen falls to 40 mm. and the carbon dioxide tension is raised to 46, the blood will be less saturated than if the carbon dioxide tension had not changed. This shift pushes an extra 1 cc. of oxygen for every 100 cc. of blood (5% saturation) into the tissues. In exercise, there is a great demand for oxygen and a large production of carbon dioxide. In this case, this shift aids greatly in getting more oxygen to the tissues.

Fixed acids have the same effect on the oxygen-hemoglobin dissociation curve as carbon dioxide. In exercise, in which lactic acid is produced, or in diabetics, in which acetoacetic and β-hydroxybutyric acids are formed, this shift aids in supplying the tissues with more oxygen.

Temperature also changes the position of the curve, the higher the temperature, the less oxygen is carried by the blood, especially venous blood. This is of aid in muscular exercise or in fever in which there is an increase in metabolism and an increased need for additional oxygen for there is a greater unloading power of the blood under these conditions.

There are *other factors* which affect the position of the curve. *Hemoglobins* from different species have different properties for saturation of oxygen. In fact, different hemoglobins may be recognized by the slope of the curve under standard conditions. The *salt content of the blood* also has a slight effect on the curve under normal conditions. When purified hemoglobin is used in the construction of the curve, the curve is shifted to the left. However, the changes in salt content of the blood are generally not of sufficient magnitude to effect any change in the property of the blood to carry hemoglobin.

Coefficient of Oxygen Utilization: The fraction of the total oxygen which is given up to the tissues is called the "coefficient of oxygen utilization." For example, if the oxygen

Speed of Oxidation of Hb.— .010 Seconds

content of the arterial blood is 20 vols. per cent and that of the venous blood is 14 vols. per cent, the coefficient of utilization is 6/20 or .30. During exercise, if the venous blood has 6 vols. per cent oxygen during exercise, the coefficient is 14/20 or 0.70. At high altitudes, the arterial saturation will fall and the coefficient will increase. At 18,000 feet, the blood is 70 per cent saturated; therefore, it contains 14.7 vols. per cent oxygen. If 6 vols. per cent are given up during the passage of the blood through the tissues, the coefficient of utilization is 6/147 or 0.41. It is obvious from these calculations that either a fall in the content of the venous blood or of the arterial blood will increase this coefficient of utilization.

Speed of Oxygenation and Reduction of Hemoglobin: Hemoglobin is an ideal molecule for carrying oxygen. It can take up oxygen with great rapidity in the lungs. The velocity of these processes has been measured. The speed of oxidation is so rapid that in .010 seconds hemoglobin is 75 per cent saturated. Reduction is slightly slower, for it requires almost 0.040 seconds to reduce the hemoglobin from a saturation of 100 per cent to 25 per cent. Reduction is more dependent on the acidity of the blood than oxidation. This factor is of importance in exercise, in which large amounts of carbon dioxide and of lactic acid are produced. In this case, the blood would unload its oxygen faster to meet the increased need.

Summary: **The ability of the hemoglobin molecule to take up oxygen is discussed. The amount of oxygen taken in is dependent on the partial pressure of oxygen in the alveolar air. Since this partial pressure falls with altitude,** ***a knowledge of the oxygen-hemoglobin dissociation curve is of utmost importance to the Flight Surgeon.***

Chapter VIII

THE CARRYING CAPACITY OF THE BLOOD FOR CARBON DIOXIDE

In addition to the transport of oxygen, the circulation serves an equally important function, the carrying of carbon dioxide from the tissues to the outside air. In the first chapter, a method was given for the calculation of the amount of carbon dioxide physically dissolved in the blood. If the absorption coefficient is multiplied by the ratio of the partial pressure to the total pressure, the amount of carbon dioxide dissolved in 1 cc. of blood may be obtained. Therefore, at 40 mm. tension, the carbon dioxide dissolved in 100 cc. of blood is 2.7 cc.

$$0.510 \times 40/760 \times 100 = 2.7 \text{ cc.}$$

However, if whole blood exposed to the same tension of carbon dioxide, 40 mm. Hg., is analyzed, 47 cc. of carbon dioxide are obtained. Therefore, there must be a chemical mechanism present for the carrying of the carbon dioxide in excess of that carried in physical solution.

Carbon Dioxide Dissociation Curve: Since the total amount of carbon dioxide carried in the blood depends on the partial pressure of carbon dioxide, dissociation curves may be constructed in a similar manner as the oxygen-hemoglobin dissociation curves (Figure 9). Two curves for this relationship are given in this figure, one for arterial blood and the other for venous blood. Therefore, these two bloods have different properties for the carrying of carbon dioxide. The problem now resolves itself in explaining (1) how carbon dioxide is chemically carried in the blood and (2) why venous blood carries more carbon dioxide than arterial blood.

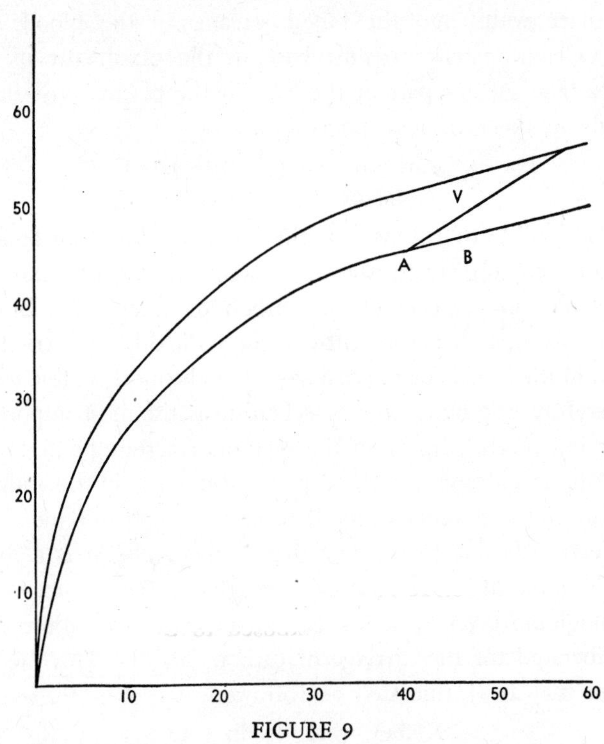

FIGURE 9

Carbon dioxide dissociation curves. Abscissa, carbon dioxide tension; ordinate, volumes per cent of carbon dioxide in blood. Upper curve, completely reduced blood, lower curve, arterial blood. A, arterial point; V, venous point; B, venous point if property of blood did not change.

Chemical Carriage of Carbon Dioxide: As soon as a molecule of carbon dioxide is found in the tissues, it combines with water to form carbonic acid.

$$CO_2 + H_2O = H_2CO_3 \qquad (1)$$

Carbonic acid ionizes to form $H^+ + HCO_3^-$

$$H_2CO_3 = H^+ + HCO_3^- \qquad (2)$$

These ions are freely diffusible and pass readily through the capillary walls into the blood stream. In the blood, the HCO_3 ion matches against base in the plasma or in the cells. The greater part of the base in the plasma is sodium, while in the cells it is potassium.

$$Na^+ \text{ (plasma) or } K^+ \text{ (cells)} + HCO_3^- = NaHCO_3 \text{ or } KHCO_3 \quad (3)$$

The ability of the base in the blood to match up against HCO_3^- coming from the cells accounts for the carrying of about 90 per cent of the carbon dioxide in the blood. It is obvious that very little carbon dioxide is carried as such in the blood for the majority is in chemical combination. Therefore, the bicarbonate mechanism is the most important carrying mechanism from the quantitative standpoint.

The second question concerns the difference in the abilities of arterial and venous bloods to carry carbon dioxide. This difference is due to the fact that oxyhemoglobin is a more acidic molecule than reduced hemoglobin. Therefore, when hemoglobin gives up its oxygen in the capillaries, more base is liberated for the carriage of carbon dioxide. This mechanism may be formulated as follows:

$$KHbO_2 = K^+ + Hb + O_2 \quad (4)$$

$$K^+ + HCO_3^- = KHCO_3 \quad (5)$$

The gain in the ability to carry carbon dioxide in the venous blood is shown graphically in Figure 9. At a given pressure of carbon dioxide in the lungs, for example 40 mm. Hg., the arterial blood will leave the lungs with 46 cc. of carbon dioxide in every 100 cc. of blood (Point A, Figure 9). When this blood leaves the tissues, the tension of carbon dioxide is now 47 mm. Hg. If the shift had not occurred, only 47 cc. would be carried; however, since it does occur, 49 cc. are carried (Point B, Figure 9). Therefore, 2 cc. additional carbon dioxide are carried in venous blood through the aid of the hemoglobin molecule.

Hemoglobin may aid in another manner in the carriage of carbon dioxide. This is through a direct combination of carbon dioxide with hemoglobin. The amino group in the protein part of the hemoglobin molecule has the property of forming a carbamate with carbon dioxide.

$$HbNH_2 + CO_2 = HbNHCOOH \quad (6)$$

It is thought that 10 per cent of the total carbon dioxide may be carried in this form. It is of interest that reduced hemoglobin may combine in this fashion with carbon dioxide more than oxygen-hemoglobin. This would aid in the carrying of extra carbon dioxide in the venous blood.

Additional Aids in the Carrying of Carbon Dioxide: Recently, it was discovered that there is an enzyme which speeds up the reaction of carbon dioxide with water and the reverse process, the breaking down of carbonic acid into carbon dioxide and water. The name "carbonic anhydrase" has been given to this enzyme. Its function, that of accelerating the loading and unloading in the blood, is a very important one. It is, however, only found in the red blood cells, not in the plasma. Therefore, those rapid changes take place only inside the red blood cell.

Another change which takes place in the blood during addition of carbon dioxide to or withdrawal from the blood is the *chloride shift*. When CO_2 enters the blood and oxygen is given up, hemoglobin becomes reduced and is more alkaline. This process liberates base and, therefore, not only does more HCO_3^- but also Cl^- come into the cell to match the base. Consequently, when carbon dioxide enters the blood, the following changes take place: (1) The bicarbonate content of cells and plasma increases; (2) the chloride content of the cells increases; (3) the chloride content of the plasma decreases. Hemoglobin acts like a piston; when it is oxygenated, it pushes Cl^- and HCO_3^- out of the cell into the plasma;

when reduced, it pulls these substances into the cell.

Another aid in the carrying of carbon dioxide is the *acidic or basic strength of the blood*. It is obvious that if more base is present, the blood will carry more carbon dioxide; if less base or other acids are present, there will be less carbon dioxide carried by the blood. Therefore, pH, a subject described in the next section, is an important factor in the carriage of carbon dioxide by the blood.

Maintenance of Neutrality by the Body: There are several mechanisms in the body which prevent the blood from becoming too acid or too alkaline. These mechanisms are of importance in aviation, for they are called upon in the maintenance of the acid-base equilibrium of the aviator flying to a high altitude.

In order to distinguish between weak and strong acids, it is necessary to have some method of designation. Although the older method of tasting these acids gave a rough classification, the newer method of determining their *dissociative constants* gives a more exact separation between the two types. This constant may be defined as a ratio between the product of the concentration of the dissociated parts of the acid and the concentration of the undissociated parts. For example, acetic acid dissociates into H^+ and CH_3COO^-. Therefore, the dissociation constant of acetic acid, Ka, is

$$\frac{[H^+]\ [CH_3COO^-]}{[CH_3COOH]} = Ka \qquad (7)$$

Dissociation constants of a few substances are given in Table 13. It may be seen in this table that HCl has a large dissociation constant while acids, such as acetic, have a small dissociation constant. This means that hydrochloric acid in water is mainly in the form of H^+ and Cl^- while acetic acid is only slightly ionized. Most of the acid remains in the form

CH_3COOH while only a few H^+ and CH_3COO^- ions are present in solution. It is obvious that a measurement of H^+ would give the acid strength. *In order to deal with small hydrogen ion concentrations, the term pH was devised.* This symbol is the negative logarithm of the hydrogen ion concentration and, therefore, converts numbers with large negative exponents into whole numbers. For example, a .001 N hy-

TABLE 13

DISSOCIATION CONSTANTS FOR VARIOUS ACIDS

Class	*Example*	*Ka*
Strong Acids	Hydrochloric Acid	1×10^{7}
Moderate	Dichloracetic Acid	5×10^{-2}
Weak	Acetic Acid	1.8×10^{-5}
Very Weak	Phenol	1×10^{-10}
Extremely Weak	Glucose	1×10^{-13}
Extremely Weak	Water	1×10^{-14}

drochloric acid solution is almost completely dissociated. Therefore, the concentration of H^+ is .001 N or 1×10^{-3} N; the logarithm of the hydrogen concentration (H^+) is, therefore, -3 or the pH is 3, the negative logarithm.

Water has a dissociation constant of 1×10^{-14}. It dissociates into H^+ and OH^- ions. The concentration of each would equal 1×10^{-7}, therefore, the pH of pure water is 7. Since this is a neutral solution, 7 can be taken as the neutral point on a pH scale, while values less than 7 are acid, having an excess of H^+ ions, and values greater than 7 show a preponderance of OH^- ions and are, therefore, basic solutions.

The pH or acid-base properties of any solution containing an acid and its salt depends on the ratio of the concentration of the salt to the acid and to the dissociation constants of the acid. The formula for the calculation of pH is:

$$pH = pKa + \log \frac{[base]}{[acid]} \qquad (8)$$

For the bicarbonate system pKa = 6.01 and the ratio of base ($NaHCO_3$) to (H_2CO_3) is 20 to 1. Therefore, the pH of such a system is:

$$pH = 6.01 + \log \frac{20}{1} \qquad (9)$$

$$pH = 6.01 + 1.30 \qquad (10)$$

$$pH = 7.31 \qquad (11)$$

Therefore, this solution is slightly alkaline. This represents the approximate ratio and pH of normal blood. If bicarbonate is ingested, the concentration of sodium bicarbonate will increase. If it increased to 24 millimoles instead of 20, the pH would rise to:

$$pH = 6.01 + \log \frac{24}{1}$$

$$= 6.01 + 1.38$$

$$= 7.39$$

Therefore, *the pH of the blood depends mainly on the ratio of bicarbonate to carbonic acid.* The bicarbonate depends, in turn, on the amount of base present in the blood while the carbonic acid content depends on the tension of CO_2 in the alveolar air.

Buffer Systems: Another factor which aids in the acid base balance is that of the buffer systems. If a strong acid, such as lactic acid, is formed in the body, it will match with the sodium (or potassium) in the bicarbonate molecule in the following manner:

$$CH_3CHOHCOOH + NaHCO_3 = CH_3CHOHCOONa + H_2CO_3$$

Since H_2CO_3 is a weaker acid than lactate, the pH of

the solution does not change appreciably. The H_2CO_3 breaks down during passage in the lung capillaries and the extra CO_2 is expired. The ability of the alkali salts of weak acids to combine with strong acids forming the alkali salts of the strong acids and the weaker acids has given rise to the term "*buffer systems.*" Such systems are the *sodium bicarbonate—carbonic acid system* described above, the *disodium phosphate—monosodium phosphate system,* and the *alkali salts* of the serum proteins and hemoglobin in the blood.

The Rôle of the Kidneys in the Maintenance of Neutrality in the Body: The kidneys play a large rôle in the acid-base balance. If acids are formed in the body, the kidneys excrete ammonia and fixed base with the acids. If alkali is ingested, this material is excreted combined with phosphate or bicarbonate. By shifting the ratio of NaH_2PO_4 to Na_2HPO_4, the body can get rid of an additional Na^+ or H^+ ion as the need may present itself.

Summary: **The carriage of carbon dioxide by the blood is described. There are three main factors in this transport: in physical solution, in the form of bicarbonate, and by means of alkali liberated from hemoglobin. The maintenance of neutrality of the body is also given consideration. The neutrality of the body is maintained by the buffer systems in the blood by respiration, and by the kidneys. Reference will be made to these changes in the description of man at high altitudes.**

CHAPTER IX

THE CONTROL OF RESPIRATION

In the previous chapters, a discussion was given of the transport of oxygen from the air to the tissues and carbon dioxide away from the tissues to the outside air. It is obvious that the demand for oxygen must vary under different conditions and the need for an increased or decreased transport of the respiratory gases would vary under exercise, lack of oxygen, increase in the carbon dioxide content of the inspired air, and many other conditions. Therefore, there must be a regulatory mechanism present to meet these needs. This regulatory mechanism is present and is given such a fine adjustment of respiratory activity that the increase of oxygen consumption during muscular exercise is met by a corresponding increase in respiratory activity.

There are two chief methods for the control of respiration: by way of the central nervous system, *the neural control;* and by means of chemical changes taking place in the blood, *the chemical control.*

Neural Control of Respiration: *Galen,* one of the first experimentalists, sectioned the brain of an animal and found that if he cut through a certain portion of the brain, respiratory activity ceased. This discovery (first century) was the first to show that respiration was dependent on a center in the brain. Galen's method of sectioning the brain has been used by many modern investigators. Their results have shown that in the upper part of the medulla there is a neurological structure which is called the respiratory center. Additional evidence has shown that this center is in that location. For example, if electrical or thermal stimuli are applied to this region, either inspiration or expiration may be produced. If electrodes are attached to this region and are connected to delicate electrical recording devices, electrical activity occurs in this region during inspiration and expiration.

Effects of Higher Centers on Respiration: Respiration may be increased or decreased through the will of the individual. This indicates that the higher centers in the cortex of the brain control respiration. We can, for example, hold our breath. This means that impulses from the higher centers must hold the respiratory center in check for a short period of time. The average person can hold his breath for one minute. However, if he breathes deeply before he holds his breath, he may be able to prolong this to two or three minutes. The world record for breath-holding is twenty-one minutes. This was obtained by having a man breathe oxygen for several minutes before the trial. The breathing of oxygen accomplishes several things: (1) it washes out the nitrogen from the body, (2) it increases the oxygen tension and supply, and (3) it washes out the carbon dioxide. The washing out of carbon dioxide and the increase in oxygen enabled this individual to hold his breath for this long period of time.

Sensory Nerves Affecting Respiration: Numerous sensory sensations affect respiration. It is well-known that pain may make a man gasp, that cold water suddenly thrown on a man changes the character of his respiratory activity. These facts illustrate that there are connections between these sensory nerves and the respiratory center. This reflex may be a primitive defensive mechanism in which pain or cold produces an increase in respiratory activity to aid the animal in fight or flight.

The Effect of the Vagi Nerves on Respiration: The vagi nerves carry impulses from and to the regions of the chest and abdomen and the brain. It is a familiar experiment in

Physiology to modify respiration by cutting these nerves. Before section, the animal will be breathing normally under the anesthetic; after section, the respiratory activity will be slower and deeper. If the central cut ends of these nerves are stimulated, respiration may stop at the end of inspiration or at the end of expiration. These experiments demonstrate a dominant control of the vagi over respiration. During every inspiration, impulses pass up the two vagi which inhibit inspiration and produce expiration. During expiration, similar impulses inhibit expiration and produce inspiration. When these impulses are cut off by sectioning the nerve, the inhibitory factors are removed and respiration becomes deeper both as to inspiration and expiration. The sensory end organs for these reflexes are in the lungs and are stimulated by the acts of stretching and contraction of the lung tissue. Physiologists refer to these reflexes mediated through the vagi nerves as the *Hering-Breuer* reflexes in honor of the men who first discovered them.

Summary of Neural Control of Respiration:* Although there may be many nerves in the body carrying impulses which may affect respiration, the three main channels are from the higher centers of the brain, the skin, and the lungs. Of these, *the impulses coming from the lungs and carried by the vagi are the most important for they control every respiratory act in the normal individual.

Chemical Control of Respiration

In contrast to the control of respiration by means of nerves is the chemical control of respiration. Respiration may be affected by the change in concentration of various substances in the blood, the two most important being carbon dioxide and oxygen.

The Effect of Carbon Dioxide on Respiration: In the classical researches of Professor Haldane, it was shown that the effects of breathing increasing concentrations of carbon dioxide up to 3 per cent had very little effect on respiration. Increasing the concentration above this point causes an increase in depth of breathing and a further increase in carbon dioxide causes an increase in rate. The primary increase in depth and the later increase in rate produce an augmentation in the amount of air moved in and out of the lungs per minute. These facts illustrate a dominant effect of carbon dioxide tension on respiratory activity. Many experiments have been carried out since Haldane's and they have all shown that respiration is very sensitive to carbon dioxide changes. In fact, so sensitive that we look upon the carbon dioxide tension in the lungs and blood as the delicate control for respiratory activity. The effect of changes in the carbon dioxide tension in the blood are mediated directly on the respiratory center. Evidence for this statement will be given after the next section is presented.

Effect of Oxygen-Lack on Respiration: Respiratory activity may, also, be modified by severe oxygen lack as well as by an increase in carbon dioxide. This oxygen lack may be produced by a number of methods which will be described in detail in the following chapter. However, greater changes in oxygen concentration in the inspired air are required to produce a change in respiration than for carbon dioxide. It was thought at one time that the lack of oxygen in blood affected the respiratory center directly, but recent work has shown this idea to be erroneous. It was through the discovery of *Heymans* that it was recognized there was an outpost in the circulation which responds to oxygen lack. This outpost is the carotid body. The carotid body is situated between the external and internal carotids just at the point of subdivision of the common carotid artery. This small body is richly supplied with blood vessels, nerve fibers, and nerve endings.

The nerve endings respond to changes in oxygen content of the blood and, therefore, are part of the controlling mechanisms to anoxia. If the carotid bodies are intact, both a carbon dioxide increase and an oxygen decrease will produce a respiratory change. If the carotid bodies are removed, then only a respiratory change is obtained with an increase in carbon dioxide. The respiratory augmentation to oxygen lack is abolished by removal of the carotid bodies. Therefore, it is obvious that there is a subdivision of control; carbon dioxide affecting the respiratory center while anoxia stimulates respiration through the carotid bodies.

Summary: **Chemical changes in the blood affect respiratory activity. The two chief chemicals which affect respiration activity are carbon dioxide and oxygen. Carbon dioxide changes are mediated directly through the respiratory center while the oxygen effect is mediated through the carotid body.**

Chapter X

THE ACUTE EFFECTS OF ANOXIA

In the preceding chapters, a description was given of the decreased barometric pressure which occurs with altitude, and how this diminished pressure lowers the driving force to get oxygen into the blood. Thus, the blood contains less oxygen when a man is at a high altitude. The lowering of the amount of oxygen in the blood and its tension decreases the amount of oxygen in the tissues, which, in turn, suffer from oxygen starvation.

Classification of Anoxia: There are many methods (Table 14) of producing oxygen starvation or anoxia in the tissues.

TABLE 14

Classification of Anoxia

Atmospheric Air	*Alveolar Air*	*Transport in Blood*	*Tissues*
		Stagnant Anoxia	Histotoxic
		Anemic Anoxia	Anoxia
	Pulmonary Membranes		
Anoxic Anoxia			

Anoxia may be classified according to these methods of production. The first type is *anoxic anoxia,* which is characterized by a lack of oxygen in the arterial blood due to the lowering of the oxygen tension. This type may be produced by decreasing the oxygen content of the inspired air, by a reduction of external pressure, by tracheal or bronchial obstruction or by decreased permeability of the pulmonary membranes. The latter change occurs in pneumonia or in pulmonary oedema. In fact, any condition which reduces pulmonary exchange would come under this classification. *

* Locked - Cranio - Sacral mechanism.

The second type is *stagnant anoxia:* This type of anoxia is produced by a failing circulation. The blood leaving the lungs is fully oxygenated, but the time of passage through the tissue capillaries is so slow that the oxygen is used from the blood before capillary circulation is completed. This type of anoxia may be seen locally in arterial or venous obstruction, in myocardial failure or in surgical shock.

The third type is the *anemic anoxia:* In this type of anoxia, there is a reduction in the hemoglobin content of the blood in such amounts that the blood is no longer able to carry sufficient oxygen to the tissues. The hemoglobin, which is present, is saturated to the normal tension when leaving the alveolar capillaries. This type may be due to an actual reduction of hemoglobin as in the primary and secondary anemias or in carbon monoxide poisoning.

The fourth and last type is the *histotoxic type:* In this type of anoxia, there is a block produced by a pharmacological agent which stops the use of oxygen in the tissues. Histotoxic anoxia is produced by such poisons as cyanide.

The changes produced by anoxia will be discussed under the headings of general changes and of special changes. In the second section, a detailed discussion will be given of the effects of anoxia on the various organ systems.

General Effects of Acute Anoxia

The best method for observing the general effects of acute anoxia is in a low pressure chamber, for in such a chamber, the observer may take oxygen and be in a position to see the changes occurring in a large number of experimental subjects. Practically, no changes are observed until altitudes above 15,000 feet are reached. At this altitude, the subject generally becomes quiet, there is a slight blue tinge to his finger nail beds, his lips and ear lobes. When 18,000 feet is reached, the blue color deepens, the individual may complain of feeling dizzy and weak, his muscular coordination is poor and he has lost his power of attention. If 20,000 feet is reached, the symptoms become worse and the individual may faint or become so mentally incoordinated that he can no longer tolerate the lowered barometric pressure and the run must be discontinued.

Similar findings are observed if an individual is given gas mixtures of low oxygen content to breathe. This was the standard method of obtaining comparative ceilings of men in the last war. The results of these tests demonstrated several important facts. In the first place, there is a marked variation among men to withstand altitude. One man may go to an equivalent altitude of 27,000 feet while the next man may become unconscious at 18,000 feet. The fact that the first man can go to 27,000 feet in a test does not mean that he could fly to that altitude. It does indicate, however, that he is much more capable of withstanding anoxia than the second man.

The second fact that came out of these tests was that a man's "ceiling" depended on his physical condition. If he is stale, has had a recent illness, or has indulged in too much alcohol, his "ceiling" is lowered. When he recovers and feels better, his ceiling returns to normal. Therefore, the rebreather test was used as a measure of physical fitness.

The third fact that was observed in these tests was that men failed at the end of the tests either because of fainting or on account of mental failure. These facts divided the men into two groups, the "fainters" and the "non-fainters." Of course, every "non-fainter" could be made into a "fainter," if taken high enough. The terminology, therefore, is taken to indicate why a run was discontinued. The "fainter" failed from either circulatory or respiratory failure, while the "non-

★ "The Brain requires 6Xs more O_2 than any other tissue — to do its work

fainter" failed because of marked and severe mental changes. It is obvious that in the first class the anoxia has affected the circulatory and respiratory centers, while in the second class, the higher centers of the brain are affected.

Dangers of Anoxia in Aviation: One of the most quoted stories of the dangers of anoxia is that of the balloon ascension of Tissandier and his two companions, Crocé and Sivel. These three men ascended from Paris in a free balloon in 1875. On reaching 22,900 feet, Tissandier wrote, "Torpor has seized me. We are rising. Body and mind become feebler. There is no suffering. On the contrary one feels an inward joy. There is no thought of the dangerous position. One rises and is glad to be rising. All at once I shut my eyes and fell down powerless and lost all further memory." The balloon ascended to 28,820 feet and then descended. On the descent Tissandier recovered. Not realizing his danger, he threw over his sandbags and went up again. On the second descent he discovered that his two companions were dead. This story illustrates several facts concerning the danger of anoxia. Tissandier describes the "inward joy" that came over him. This is characteristic of the insidious nature of anoxia. The individual is not aware of his danger. Tissandier also carried out an irrational deed; he threw over the sandbags and ascended a second time. This irrational act probably cost the lives of his two companions.

Another story illustrating the irrational deeds that men carry out was told to the author by Dr. Bazett. In the last war a man was sent on a photographic mission to 22,000 feet. On his return, it was found that his plates were fogged. The aviator blamed the man in the developing room, claiming that this man fogged the plates on purpose. On examination of the camera, however, it was found that the aviator had opened his camera and had urinated into it when he was at his maximum altitude.

Maland Thomas - Montoursville, Pa
Air Force Gunner World War II described to me only Last week the Greatest Thrill he ever had ("better than interc.") was in Tank (Altitude)

Many other stories could be told of sudden collapse in planes, of planes falling out of formation, of radio signals ceasing, of the inability of the pilot to fly a course on mapping missions, and of bombs dropped on the wrong target. These dangerous changes may have been due to anoxia in the man.

Special Effects of Acute Anoxia

A discussion will now be given of the effects of anoxia on the various organ systems of the body.

Respiratory Effect: The depth of breathing increases in order to get more oxygen into the lungs. This may start in some individuals as low as 6,000 feet, in others, it may not change until 15,000 feet is reached. Respiration may be irregular and Cheyne-Stokes type of breathing may predominate. The latter type of respiration is characterized by a gradual increase in amplitude followed by a decrease with periods of apnoea. On the Jungfrau, at 12,000 feet, individuals have been heard to snore with this type of breathing. The rate of breathing is not affected as much as the depth.

The augmentation of breathing is caused by stimulation of the carotid body through the lack of oxygen in the blood. When there is this stimulation, the fine regulation of respiration, due to carbon dioxide control, changes to a regulatory mechanism run by anoxia. The carbon dioxide tension of the body falls which aids in the carrying capacity of the blood for oxygen. For every mm. of fall of carbon dioxide, there is a corresponding rise in oxygen tension. The blood, as a result, becomes more alkaline. This fact will be discussed again in Chapter XII.

Circulatory Changes: The pulse rate increases at 18,000 feet in a low pressure chamber, with an average increase of 20 beats per minute. This rise in pulse indicates that additional blood is being pumped out of the heart per minute. The speeding up of the circulation aids in carrying more blood to the tissues per unit of time. However, it does place additional strain on the heart. The coronary arteries dilate to meet the need of more oxygen to the active heart muscle. This strain may be so great that the heart may not meet the demand and fail. Another factor contributing to the failure is the drop of diastolic blood pressure. Diastolic blood pressure is regulated by the tone of the capillaries and arterioles which, in turn, are dependent on the vasomotor center in the brain stem. When the latter center suffers severely from the lack of oxygen, diastolic pressure falls. Systolic pressure will, also, fall when the heart is unable to pump out sufficient blood. Therefore, circulatory collapse is due to two factors; a central mechanism, the vasomotor center failure; and a peripheral mechanism, cardiac failure.

Mental Changes: With the fall in the driving force to get oxygen into the blood and the resultant loss of oxygen in the blood, there is a decrease in mental ability. The brain is the most sensitive organ to the lack of oxygen. Every aviator who has flown to high altitudes and every mountaineer who has climbed to great heights has noticed these changes. The primary effect in the majority of individuals is lassitude. This may be observed in the low pressure chamber. The men, at 18,000 feet, lose interest in their surroundings, sit still with a fixed, tired expression and are mentally and physically slowed down. A few go to the opposite extreme, laugh, talk and make purposeless movements.

Many different types of psychological tests have been applied to these men. The results have shown that anoxia does cause mental retardation, a slowing of reaction time and a decrease in the ability to concentrate on a problem. From these results it can easily be seen that a man's ability to fly a plane would be markedly decreased when suffering from anoxia. The insidious nature of this phenomenon is that the man does not realize how retarded he is when he is in an anoxic state. He thinks that everything is fine and does not realize the danger at high altitudes. Aviators must be taught the insidious nature of the mental changes that affect them when they attempt to fly to a high altitude without extra oxygen.

Visual Changes: In addition to the numerous studies made on mental changes in lowered barometric pressure, there have been many observations made on visual changes. The retina of the eye is composed of a large number of nerve cells and these cells are very susceptible to anoxia. The changes noted in the visual mechanism are impairment in the visual sensitivity and in dark adaptation, a decrease in the peripheral fields, a weakness of the extraocular muscles, a decrease in the range of accommodation, and an incoordination of ocular movements.

Other Senses: The sense of hearing, taste, smell, and touch are not affected to the same degree as the visual sensations. In fact, the sense of hearing does not go until the man is almost unconscious, although the ability to react to auditory stimuli fails early.

Types of Failure: All men, if placed in an environment of decreasing barometric pressure, will eventually lose consciousness. This failure through loss of consciousness takes on several forms. There may be a simple loss of consciousness characterized by no previous symptoms. An observer may be watching the man closely and will be unaware that the man is suffering from the effects of the lack of oxygen until he falls forward. In another individual, there is marked pallor, sweating, and a slow pulse. This individual may feel so weak and dizzy that he will warn the observer. However, by the time the observer reaches him to give him oxygen, he is unconscious. In the third type, there may be marked convulsions, while in the fourth type, there is respiratory arrest. Fortunately, the latter two are rare types.

The most serious are the convulsive and the respiratory failure types. In the convulsive type, an individual whose brain is already suffering from the lack of oxygen makes marked muscular movements causing additional oxygen to be utilized. This sets up a vicious cycle which would soon be terminated by death. The respiratory failure type needs immediate artificial respiration in addition to extra oxygen and an increase in barometric pressure.

Carbon Monoxide Anoxia

There is another type of anoxia which is of interest to aviators. That is the anoxia produced by carbon monoxide, an anemic anoxia, a combination of carbon monoxide with hemoglobin. Carbon monoxide has a marked affinity for hemoglobin, the affinity being 210 times that of oxygen. Therefore, a very small amount of carbon monoxide will saturate the blood. In the competition for the hemoglobin, carbon monoxide wins.

$$\left.\begin{array}{l}(1\text{ part})\ CO + Hb\\(210\text{ parts})\ O_2 + Hb\end{array}\right\rangle = HbCO + HbO_2$$

A dissociation curve of carbon monoxide hemoglobin (Figure 10) may be constructed in the same manner as an oxygen hemoglobin dissociation curve. From the relationship given above, it is obvious that the amount of carbon monoxide hemoglobin formed depends on the amount of oxygen present. The presence of carbon monoxide causes the oxyhemoglobin curve to shift to the left. Therefore, in an individual suffering from carbon monoxide poisoning, the oxygen saturation falls more rapidly and has less tension on the venous side to drive oxygen into the tissues. If a patient suffering from this type of anoxia tries to exercise, he will collapse very quickly from inadequate oxygenation of his tissues. Carbon dioxide, also, has the power of causing the dissociation of carbon monoxide hemoglobin. Therefore, if carbon dioxide and oxygen therapy are available, these two

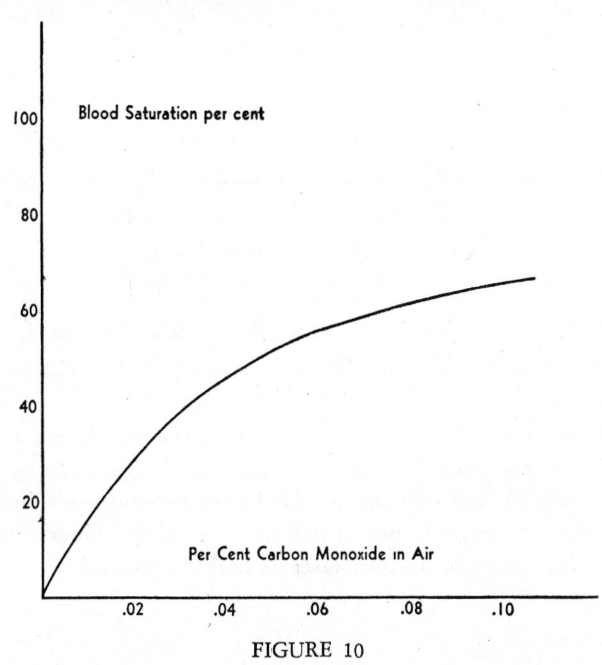

FIGURE 10

Carbon monoxide concentration and saturation of blood with carbon monoxide hemoglobin. Ordinate, saturation of blood in per cent; abscissa, concentration of carbon monoxide in air in per cent.

gases will more quickly free carbon monoxide from the hemoglobin molecule than if air is breathed.

Concentrations of Carbon Monoxide Necessary to Produce Symptoms: It is thought that man is able to withstand 0.02 per cent carbon monoxide for an indefinite period of time while he may be able to withstand 0.03 for a matter of hours. These are sea-level values. The dangers of acute anoxia from these values would become greater in an aviator flying to

TABLE 15

SYMPTOMS PRODUCED BY VARIOUS CONCENTRATIONS OF CARBON MONOXIDE

Concentration per cent	*Symptoms*
0.01	None
0.04	Headache, Weakness, Dizziness, Nausea
0.06	Increased pulse rate. Danger of collapse
0.08	Fainting. Collapse
0.10	Coma. Convulsions. Death

15,000 feet without extra oxygen. In this case, the tension of oxygen would fall with an increase in the amount of hemoglobin combined with carbon monoxide.

Summary: **The fall in barometric pressure decreases the driving force to get oxygen into the blood. The lowered oxygen tension and content of the blood produces respiratory, circulatory, mental, and visual changes. If the blood oxygen falls low enough, unconsciousness and death result.**

CHAPTER XI

THE USE OF OXYGEN IN AVIATION

In order to combat the effects of acute anoxia described in the preceding chapter, extra oxygen must be supplied to the aviator if he is to be kept both mentally and physically capable of carrying out his duties while flying at altitudes above 12,000 feet. There are two types of oxygen equipment, the ideal, which we do not possess at this time, and the type of oxygen equipment in use at the present time. Much attention is now being given to this problem and our present-day equipment will be modified to approach the ideal type of oxygen equipment.

The Ideal Oxygen Equipment: The ideal type of apparatus should have the following characteristics:

(1) It should give adequate oxygen at any altitude that the plane may reach.

(2) There should be no resistance to breathing.

(3) The apparatus should not waste oxygen.

(4) The mask should fit perfectly.

(5) There should be minimal dead space.

(6) The carbon dioxide should be removed from the inspired air.

(7) There should be a safety valve in case of failure.

(8) Speaking should not be interfered with.

(9) The apparatus should be light in weight.

(10) Moving parts should be kept to a minimum.

(11) It should work in any position.

(12) It should not be affected by extremes of temperature. We do not possess this type of equipment at the present time.

The Present Methods of Carrying Oxygen in Planes: There are three general methods of storing oxygen. It can either be compressed in its gaseous form in cylinders, or be carried in liquid form, or be liberated from a chemical compound of oxygen. Although numerous experiments have been made to use the latter two methods, the only practical method at the present time is compressed gaseous oxygen. Oxygen is compressed at 1800 pounds per square inch into cylinders varying in length from 9 inches to 53 inches. Gaseous oxygen compressed to 1800 pounds per square inch is a potential danger to military aircraft. When such a cylinder is hit by a .50 caliber bullet, the cylinder may explode. If penetrated by a 0.30 caliber, the heat of penetration may be sufficient to ignite the metal and the combustion is continued by the pressure of oxygen flowing through the hole in the cylinder. Oxygen stored at 400 pounds per square inch does not have this explosive or fire hazard. Special, non-explosive cylinders have, also, been constructed in order to avoid the explosive hazard.

The Present Methods of Administration of Oxygen: In contrast to the ideal type of oxygen equipment are the present types used in the Army and Navy. There are three general types of apparatus for supplying oxygen to an aviator: *continuous flow, the demand, and the rebreather methods. In the continuous flow type,* the oxygen is passed through a reducing valve which reduces the pressure to 3 or 4 pounds per square inch and then the oxygen flows through a rubber tube to the man. In the older methods, the oxygen was fed into the aviator's mouth through a pipe stem; in the newer methods, it is passed into a mask and the man breathes the oxygen flowing into the mask. It is obvious that this method is very wasteful of oxygen for it gives oxygen not only during inspiration when the man needs oxygen, but also during expiration when oxygen is not needed. There is, also, danger of the pipe stem falling from the man's mouth, causing the man to suffer acutely from anoxia. The pressure of the tube in the man's mouth causes salivation. This fact led aviators to term the pipe stem a "dribble tube."

Since the continuous flow apparatus proved to be very inefficient, numerous other types of oxygen equipment have been devised. One of these, *the demand type,* has proven to be more efficient. In this type, there is a valve which opens when the man breathes in, allowing oxygen to reach him. This same valve closes when the man breathes out, and his expired air passes out through two valves in his mask. The valve which opens and closes with each respiration must be designed to operate with a minimal amount of pressure in order not to cause discomfort to the individual.

The B.L.B. mask (Boothby, Lovelace, Bulbulian) *is a modification of the demand type.* This apparatus does not have mechanical valves, but depends for its operation on the comparative resistance between the gas in a rubber bag and the passage of gas through a sponge rubber valve. Oxygen is led into the bag. The subject breathes from the bag and the resistance is such that the oxygen will come from the bag before air will be admitted through the sponge rubber. At lower altitudes, some air does come through the sponge rubber, but this is an advantage for it saves oxygen. At higher altitudes, the expansion of gases is so great that the distension of the bag increases the force on the oxygen supply from the bag. Therefore, gas is supplied only from the bag at high altitudes. When the man breathes out, the initial force of expiration fills the bag. As soon as the bag is filled, the comparative resistance between bag and valve is such that the remainder of the expired air passes out through the sponge rubber valves. For hospital use, for heated cabin planes, and for pressure chamber work, this apparatus works perfectly. However, there is danger of the sponge rubber valves freezing in unheated planes and there is, also, danger if the individual takes deeper breaths as in muscular exertion for the sponge rubber valves may admit outside air. Therefore, the B.L.B. is not entirely suited for military purposes.

Other forms of demand types have valves which admit a mixture of air and oxygen in order to save oxygen at lower altitudes where 100 per cent oxygen is not needed.

The demand type, also, wastes oxygen. When 100 per cent oxygen is supplied by this type, only 5 per cent is converted into carbon dioxide and 95 per cent of the inspired oxygen is wasted during expiration. *In the rebreather type,* this expired oxygen is breathed back into a bag from which it may be rebreathed. It is obvious that in this type there must be valves to direct the flow and a canister filled with carbon dioxide and water vapor absorbent. This makes a bulky apparatus which is subjected to mechanical breakdown and an unknown accumulation of nitrogen in the circuit. If air is admitted to the system or if nitrogen is liberated from the body, it will circulate and dilute the oxygen supply. Since the oxygen will be used, the nitrogen content will increase. Therefore, the rebreather type must be washed out regularly in order to get rid of any nitrogen present. This is done by breathing through a valve to the outside air two or three times following in from the apparatus.

For patrol work, in which flights to extreme altitudes are not made and in which large numbers of crew members may be present, the rebreather type is ideal, for it is most economical in its use of oxygen. However, it would not be useful in fighter planes going to very high altitudes, since it has the possibility of nitrogen collecting in the circuit and lowering the ceiling of the man to an unknown and variable extent.

Need for Oxygen at Various Altitudes: The regulations in the Army and Navy call for oxygen to be used by all flying personnel above 12,000 feet, although the exact altitude varies with the time at that altitude. However, oxygen should be used at lower altitudes during long flights or at night. Night vision is especially susceptible to anoxia and oxygen should be used at 6,000 feet or above while flying at night. One hundred per cent oxygen is not needed until altitudes of 30,000 feet are reached.

Above 34,000 feet, at which the barometric pressure is 187.4 mm. Hg., pure oxygen can no longer maintain air oxygen pressure of 159 for the total barometric pressure is less than this value and, therefore, the aviator becomes anoxic even though he is breathing 100 per cent oxygen. In practice, pure oxygen should be given at 30,000 feet. In fact, if a man received 100 per cent oxygen, he should be as efficient at 34,000 feet as at sea level. For, at 34,000 feet, his oxygen tension in his lungs would be approximately 100 mm. Hg., the same as at sea level. However, if he goes higher, his oxygen tension will fall, due to the fall in barometric pressure. For example, at 42,000 feet, the total barometric pressure is 127. In his lungs, carbon dioxide will take up approximately 35 mm. of this pressure and water vapor will take up 47 mm. Therefore, only 45 mm. [127 − (35 + 47)] would be left over for oxygen. At this pressure (Figure 11), the blood is only 79 per cent saturated which corresponds to the saturation at an altitude of 16,000 feet breathing air. Therefore, 40,000 feet is considered the limit for man using the present oxygen equipment.

Time of Survival Following Failure of Oxygen Supply: The time of survival without oxygen has been estimated for various altitudes. At 40,000 feet a man would have one minute before he became unconscious; at 35,000 feet, he would have three minutes; while, at 20,000 feet, he may last fifteen minutes. These facts illustrate the need for oxygen during a parachute jump from high altitudes. If a man should

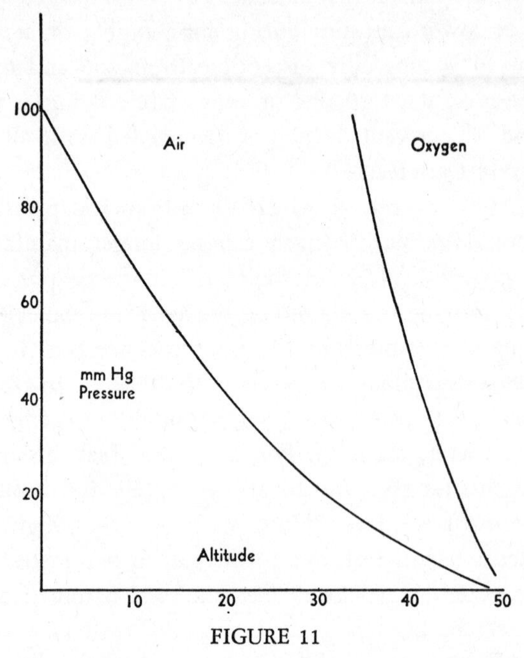

FIGURE 11

The alveolar oxygen saturation at various altitudes while breathing air and breathing oxygen. Ordinate, alveolar oxygen pressure in mm. Hg.; abscissa, altitude in thousands of feet.

jump out of his plane at 40,000 feet and pull the rip cord, he would descend at the rate of 1,500 feet per minute. It would take him 10 minutes to reach 25,000 feet and he would be dead from anoxia as a result. If he should come down in a free fall, he might be still conscious when he passed the 25,000 foot level, but would be suffering from anoxia. Therefore, for men flying to such altitudes, an emergency supply of oxygen must be taken and a means supplied for connecting this suppy to his mask before jumping.

The Need for Pressure Cabin or Pressure Suits in the Stratosphere: The world's record for an open cockpit plane is held by Donati, an Italian, who reached an altitude calculated on a density basis of 47,538 feet. Man has flown much higher using a pressure suit. With this equipment, altitudes of 54,000 feet have been reached. This record was made several years ago and the absolute ceilings of the present military planes have never been published. However, with the tremendous increase in plane design, the ceilings are probably much higher than those given above. In the preceding sections, it was stated that the ceiling for man using oxygen equipment is about 40,000 feet. If altitudes above this value are to be reached, the man must be placed in a pressure cabin or a pressure suit. Both methods would keep the pressure around the man at a value in which his blood would be kept saturated with oxygen. However, both methods present engineering difficulties. With the pressure suits, the difficulty is in getting joints which will withstand the pressure as well as give motility. In the pressure cabins, there are problems of maintenance of the pressure at a safe level, temperature regulation, elimination of carbon dioxide and other noxious gases, humidity control, and many others. There is always the danger of explosive decompression if any damage occurs to the cabin. The solution may be found in a combination of oxygen and pressure. Oxygen may be supplied to the man at the existing external barometric pressure until altitudes around 34,000 feet are reached. Then the pressure will be kept in the suit or cabin equivalent to 34,000 feet (190 mm.) while the plane ascends to higher altitudes. It would be necessary, of course, to maintain a 100 per cent oxygen supply to the aviator. In this manner, the man would not suffer any effect from the decreasing barometric pressure above 34,000 feet.

***Summary:* A description is given of the various types of apparatus used in supplying oxygen to aviators. No type is perfect and intensive research is now being carried on to improve these methods. The need for oxygen in aviation is stressed. For altitudes above 40,000 feet, either pressure cabins or pressure suits will be needed.**

CHAPTER XII

THE CHRONIC EFFECTS OF ALTITUDE

The requirements for taking oxygen require that oxygen shall be taken above 12,000 feet. The question is frequently raised that men live and work at altitudes considerably above this height without extra oxygen. The answer to this question is that these men are acclimatized to these altitudes. The mechanism of acclimatization is mainly respiratory and circulatory.

Methods of Study: It is interesting to note that man did not realize the dangers of high altitudes until after the discovery of this continent. It was Acosta, a Spanish priest, who accompanied the early explorers in South America and who first described mountain sickness and attributed these findings to altitude and not to the effects of cold or winds. However, it was not until the middle of the last century that any attempt was made to study these changes scientifically. This was done by *Paul Bert,* the great French physiologist. In his book, *La Pression Barométrique,* published in 1878, Bert collected stories from mountain climbers on the effects of altitude, listed the number of inhabitants of the world living at great heights and described his experiments made at high and low pressures in experimental chambers. In more recent times, much interest has been taken in this subject. Parties of physiologists have been organized to live at altitudes of 14,000 feet for several weeks. During their stay, they have made observations on themselves. Laboratories have been established on mountains in order that continuous records may be made on man living at these altitudes for long periods of time. Therefore, our information concerning the chronic effects of altitude on man has come from these four sources.

The Ability of Man to Live and Work at High Altitudes: It is estimated that there are 10,000,000 inhabitants of this globe living at altitudes of 10,000 feet or more. In the mining camps of South America, men live at 17,000 feet and work at 18,000 feet. There are monasteries in Tibet where the monks spend their lives at 17,000 feet. It is interesting to note that the miners in South America prefer to live at 17,000 feet and to walk up the additional 1,000 feet to work each day, rather than to live at 18,000 feet. Although an attempt was made to live at 18,000 feet, it was abandoned, and these men moved down to 17,000 feet. This indicates that the limit for acclimatization for man is between 17,000 and 18,000 feet.

A classic description of the changes occurring at altitudes is given by Haldane in his record of his experiences on Pike's Peak. "Many persons walked or rode up during the night to see the sunrise, especially on Sunday morning, and the scene in the restaurant and on the platform outside can only be likened to that on the deck or in the cabin of a cross-channel steamer during rough weather. The walkers straggle in one by one, looking blue, cold, exhausted, and miserable, often hurrying out again to vomit. Some lay on the floor, blue and faint. Others were able to swallow some coffee, but very few had the heart to look at the magnificent sunrise." Later, Haldane states: "Among healthy persons, it appeared invariably to be the case that after a stay of two or more days on the summit, the blueness, headache, nausea, and lack of appetite completely disappeared, while the excessive hypernoea on exertion became less. It was thus perfectly clear that acclimatization to the low pressure occurred to a very marked extent."

The Chronic Effect of Altitude on Respiration: The description given above illustrates several fundamental changes had taken place in the bodies of these men. The first change is respiratory. In Bancroft's party at Cerro de Pasco in Peru (14,200 feet) there were marked changes in the amount of air breathed in and out of the lungs per minute. In some individuals this value changed from 6.49 liters per minute at sea level to 10.00 liters per minute at 14,200 feet. Therefore, the first change in respiration is an increase in the amount of air breathed per minute under resting conditions. Work brings out even a greater change. If a man works at a rate requiring two liters of oxygen at sea level, he will breathe about 35 liters of air per minute in order to get the two liters of oxygen to his tissues. However, if he does the same work at 12,000 feet he breathes in and out 80 liters of air per minute. Therefore, even in an acclimatized subject, there is marked respiratory effort at high altitude. In the Everest climbs, one author describes seven to eight respirations for each step forward. There is increased difficulty in holding the breath at high altitudes (Fig. 12).

The increase in ventilation causes the carbon dioxide of the alveolar air and of the body to decrease. The highest recorded alveolar air sample taken in an acclimatized individual was at 26,000 feet on an Everest climb. In this individual, the carbon dioxide tension of his alveolar air was 9 mm. Hg. The lowering of carbon dioxide in the alveolar air aids in the transport of oxygen, since for every mm. of carbon dioxide tension that is lost, an equivalent mm. of oxygen tension is gained.

The blowing off of the carbon dioxide from the body makes the blood more alkaline, since the alkalinity depends on the ratio of bicarbonate to carbonic acid. Decreasing the carbonic acid content increases this ratio and thus the body becomes more alkaline. The kidneys excrete extra base to bring this ratio back to normal. Therefore, it may be said that the kidneys also aid in acclimatization. However, the adjustment is not perfect and values of the pH of the blood of 7.59 have been recorded, whereas in the same individual at sea level, 7.46 was observed.

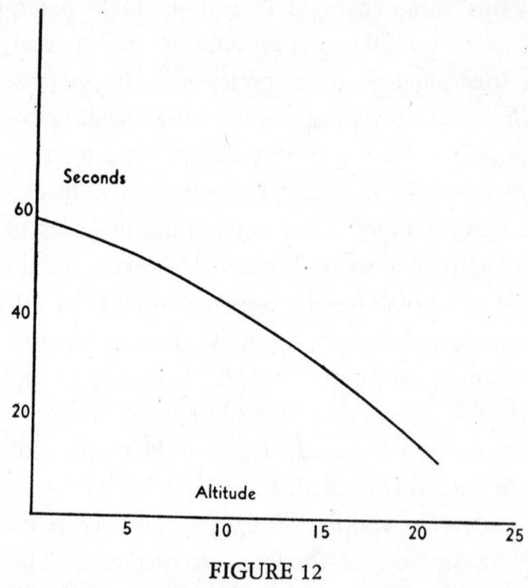

FIGURE 12
Time for holding of the breath at various altitudes. Ordinate, seconds; abscissa, altitude in thousands of feet.

The Chronic Effect of Altitude on the Circulation: Many records have been made of pulse rate at high altitudes. The basal pulse rate (Figure 14) does not change until altitudes of 15,000 feet or more are reached. Then, there is a slight increase in the basal pulse rate. If the individual attempts to work, however, there is a much greater increase in pulse rate than for an equivalent amount of work at sea level. The fact that the pulse rate does increase indicates that the cardiac output is increased. Actual measurements have shown that to be the case. On Pike's Peak, the cardiac output increased from four to six liters per minute during the first two days and then returned to its normal value. At a slightly higher

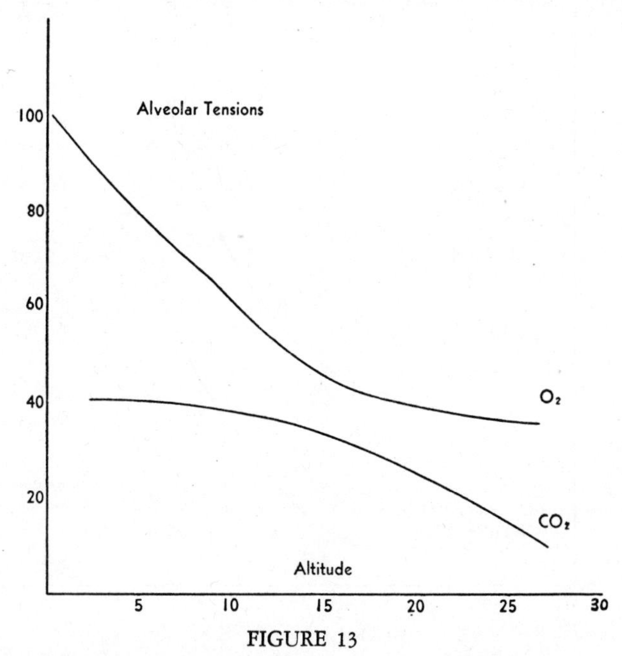

FIGURE 13

Alveolar oxygen (upper curve) and carbon dioxide (lower curve) tensions at various altitudes. Ordinate, pressure in mm. Hg.; abscissa, altitude in thousands of feet.

altitude, it was found that the cardiac output gave a similar initial rise, but did not return to the base line and remained constant around 5.0 liters per minute. These facts indicate that other methods of compensation take the load off the heart after a few days at a high altitude. Basal blood pressure does not vary much from the sea level values. This has been the experience of numerous observers making observations during mountain climbing.

The Chronic Effects of Altitude on the Blood: The most pronounced effects occur in the red blood cells. These cells

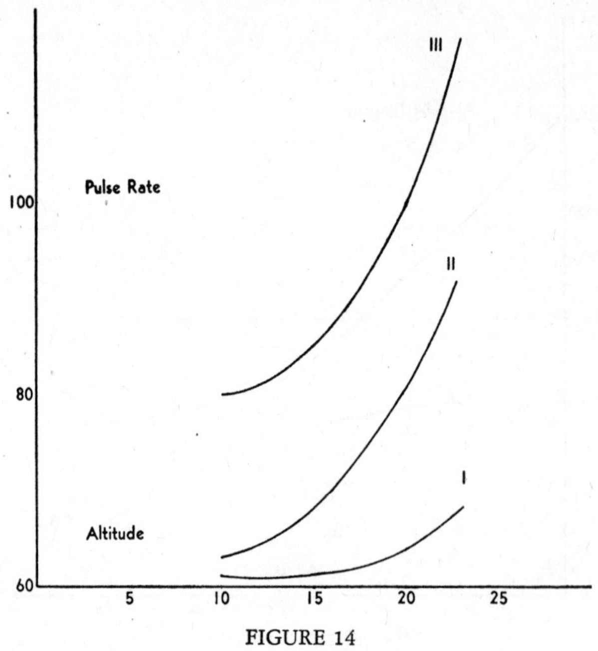

FIGURE 14

Relationship between pulse rate and altitude. I, basal pulse rate; II, sitting pulse rate; and III, standing pulse rate. Ordinate, pulse rate per minute; abscissa, altitude in thousands of feet.

increase in number (Figure 15), become larger and there is more hemoglobin per unit of blood. These remarkable changes aid greatly in the transport of oxygen in the acclimatized subject. The increase in red blood cells and hemoglobin is very rapid. Bancroft describes measurements of hemoglobin in the blood increasing from 100 per cent to 130 per cent after a four day stay at 12,600 feet. The red blood cell count may increase to 8,000,000 per cm. mm. of blood.

Another interesting change is the increase in size of the red blood cells. Instead of being the usual 7 micra, the size increases to 8 or 9 micra. The increase in size may aid in

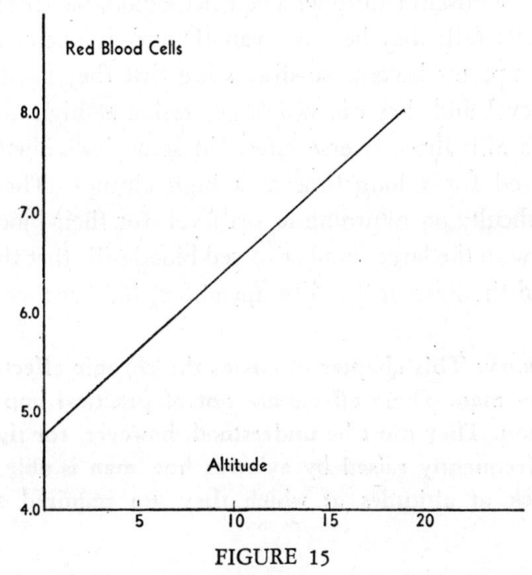

FIGURE 15

Relationship between red blood cells in millions per cubic millimeter and altitude in thousands of feet.

the carrying of oxygen for the hemoglobin molecules would have more surface for the absorption of oxygen.

The Chronic Effects of Altitude on the Mind: In spite of the changes described above which aid in the transport of oxygen, they are not adequate to supply the brain with sufficient oxygen. There is a chronic sense of fatigue and lassitude. The ability to concentrate on a given job is less. Judgment becomes more difficult. Therefore, *although the body has the capacity of partially meeting the effects of lowered* *barometric pressure, man is not mentally well at high altitudes.*

Monge's Disease: Monge, who investigated the effects of high altitude on natives of South America, has described an interesting condition in which these individuals lose their ability to withstand altitude. Their hemoglobin and red blood cell counts fall; they become cyanotic and dyspneic. In fact, these symptoms become so distressing that they must return to sea level and they can no longer reside at high altitudes. There is also the converse effect, in some individuals, who have lived for a long time at a high altitude. These men have difficulty on returning to sea level, for their blood is so viscous with the large number of red blood cells that the extra strain on the heart makes life uncomfortable for them at sea level.

Summary: **This chapter discusses the chronic effects of altitude on man. These effects are not of practical importance in aviation. They must be understood, however, for the question is frequently raised by aviators how man is able to live and work at altitudes at which they are required to take oxygen.**

CHAPTER XIII

AEROEMBOLISM

The modern development of the plane with its rapid rate of climb to high altitudes has produced a new condition in the aviator. This condition has been termed aeroembolism. It is produced by the liberation of bubbles from the fluid of the body. The liberation of gas, in turn, is caused by the rapid decrease in pressure that the man is subjected to while going to a high altitude.

A similar condition has been studied intensively in divers and in caisson workers. There is an increase in pressure on the body of man of one atmosphere for every 33 feet that he descends in sea water. Therefore, if a man is working at a depth of 200 feet, his body becomes saturated with gases at the pressure of 7 atmospheres. If this man were suddenly pulled to the surface, his circulation must carry a large amount of gas to his lungs which was formerly dissolved at the pressure of 7 atmospheres. If the circulation was adequate and the time of ascent slow, the gas may stay in solution. However, if these two factors are inadequate gas will be liberated in the form of bubbles. It is the collection of these bubbles in the blood vessels which blocks off circulation and causes the pain.

The same condition occurs in the aviator. At sea level, the gas in the body is under 1 atmosphere of pressure and it is estimated that from 800 to 1,000 cc. of nitrogen are dissolved in the body. If this man ascends to 34,000 feet where the barometric pressure is one-fourth of the sea level value, the body must rid itself of from 600 to 750 cc. of nitrogen (Fig. 16). Again, as in the case of a diver, if the ascent is very slow and the circulation adequate, the nitrogen will be carried in solution to the lungs and be eliminated. However, for military purposes, rapid ascents must be made. In

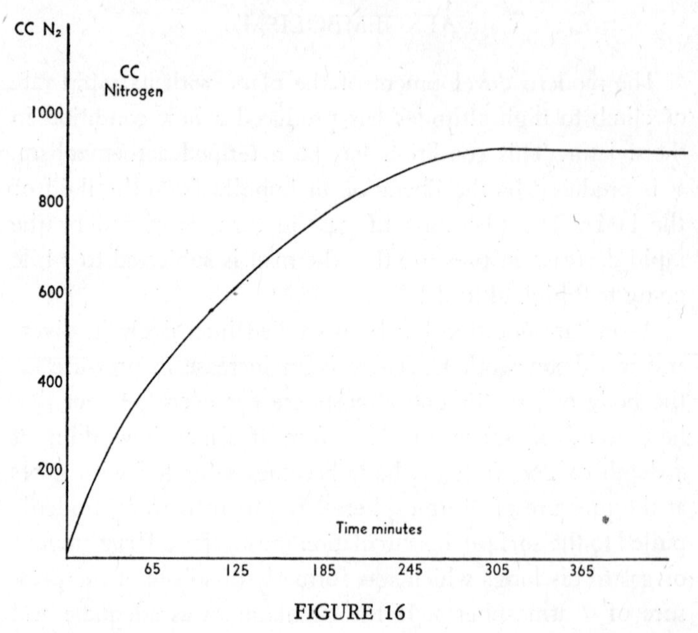

FIGURE 16

Nitrogen eliminated during the breathing of pure oxygen. Abscissa, time in minutes; ordinate, nitrogen in cc.

this case bubbles form and give rise to the signs and symptoms of aeroembolism.

Symptoms of Aeroembolism: The symptoms of aeroembolism depend on the location at which the bubbles of gas collect. The symptoms are so common in caisson workers that slang terms have been applied to them. One of the more common of the symptoms is the "itch." With the collection of the bubbles under the skin, there is itching which may be accompanied by reddening and elevation of the skin. Hot and cold sensations may be present in the affected region. Another symptom is the "bends." In these cases joint pain is present due to the collection of bubbles in these localities. The subject may feel a slight pain around a joint, which will be followed by such sharp pain that the man will hold the affected joint with this hand and splint it against his side. This is one of the incapacitating features of aeroembolism. It is obvious that a man would be unable to pilot a plane under these conditions. The pain may radiate into the skin area around the joint. It may disappear. However, the more common change is for other joints to be affected.

If aeroemboli form in the brain "staggers" may result. This condition is due to bubbles forming in the motor area or in the spinal cord. Any part of the central nervous system may be affected with symptoms characteristic of the anatomical location. The lungs may, also, be affected producing the "chokes," since pulmonary emboli may give rise to asthmatic attacks. Coronary pain may, also, result from emboli in the coronary vessels. Fortunately for the aviator, joint pain is the most common symptom. It is so acute that the man receives adequate warning of the onset of the condition.

Treatment of Aeroembolism: The obvious treatment of aeroembolism is to increase the pressure on the man in order to force the bubbles back into solution. In experimental work, a quick descent from 35,000 to 20,000 feet in the low pressure chamber is sufficient to cause the disappearance of the pain.

Another method of treatment is preventive. In the discussion above reference was made to air or gas bubbles. These bubbles, however, are mainly composed of nitrogen. All of the gases are liberated from physical solution when the atmospheric pressure is reduced. The oxygen, however, is soon taken out of the bubbles through combination with hemoglobin and the carbon dioxide combines with the alkali in the blood. Therefore, the chief constituents of the gas bubbles are nitrogen and water vapor. If the nitrogen could be removed from the body, there would be very little opportunity for aeroemboli to form in the blood stream. Therefore, if a man breathes oxygen before the ascent his chances of the development of this condition are decreased. The length of time that a man must breathe oxygen depends on the individual and the altitude that he will ascend in his flight. Exercise will aid in the removal of nitrogen by increasing the circulation time and, thereby allowing more nitrogen to be brought to the lungs in a given time.

Although rules for the time of breathing oxygen and exercise have been formulated, they do not prevent aeroemboli in all cases. The difficulty lies in the fact that the nitrogen is liberated from the body in two phases (Figure 16); a fast phase followed by a slow phase. The fast phase is due to the nitrogen coming from the water parts of the body. The slow phase is produced by the liberation of nitrogen from the fatty tissues in which circulation is slow and the amounts of nitrogen present are relatively greater than in the water of the body due to the increased solubility of nitrogen in fat. Exercise and the breathing of oxygen will eliminate in a short time about 50 per cent of the nitrogen but it requires from five to six hours to eliminate the remainder. Therefore, for long flights at high altitudes, nitrogen would come off from the fatty tissues and cause trouble. Exercise for one-half hour with breathing of pure oxygen may prevent aeroembolism in some individuals but not in all. The more susceptible individuals must be discovered before attempting high altitude flights. This may be done by trial runs in the low pressure chamber. Such classification is not needed if flights below 30,000 feet are contemplated, since it has been stated that severe symptoms of aeroembolism do not occur until altitudes above 30,000 feet are reached.

Summary: Aeroembolism, a condition caused by the collection of gaseous nitrogen in the body is discussed. The production of these aeroemboli is due to the change of pressure on the aviator as he ascends to altitudes over 30,000 feet. The treatment is to increase this pressure by a descent in order that the gas is forced back into solution. Partial prevention is obtained by breathing oxygen before an ascent.

Chapter XIV

THE CIRCULATION

In addition to a knowledge of respiration, an understanding of the circulation is necessary in order that the stresses and strains on man in flight may be thoroughly understood. For it is this system that must make many readjustments in man flying to a high altitude, during acceleration, exercise and flights of long duration.

The Cardiac Cycle: The cardiac cycle starts with the impulse originating at the sino-auricular node, passing through the auricle and reaching the atrio-ventricular node. As the impulse passes through the auricles, the auricles contract. On reaching the atrio-ventricular node, the impulse passes through the Purkinje system, a specialized condition tissue in the ventricles. As soon as the pressure is increased in the muscle, the muscles contract which increases the pressure in the ventricles. Following this increase of pressure in the ventricles, the atrio-ventricular valves (mitral and tricuspid) close and the pressure rises sharply in the ventricles until the pressure in the pulmonary and aortic vessels is reached. At this point the pulmonary and aortic valves open and blood is ejected into the vessels. The ventricles continue to contract through this ejection phase, forcing the blood pressure up and causing an augmented flow throughout the lungs and the body. The ventricles start to relax (diastole) and the pressure falls, which causes the pulmonary and aortic valves to close. Following their closure, there is a continuous relaxation of the ventricle until venous pressure is reached. At this point the atrio-ventricular valves open and blood again flows into the ventricles.

In a slowly beating heart, the beating of the auricles contributes very little to the filling of the ventricles since the ventricles are almost completely filled before the auricles contract. The flow of bood into the ventricles floats the atrio-ventricular valves almost into place so that the beginning of ventricular contraction is sufficient to close these valves. The closure of the aortic valves causes a reflected wave of pressure throughout the arterial system. This wave may be recorded graphically and is called the *dicrotic notch.*

The Pressure Changes in the Circulation: The period of contraction following the closure of the atrio-ventricular valves and before the opening of the aortic valves is called the *presphygmic phase;* the period during which the aortic valves are open is called the *sphygmic phase;* while the period of relaxation is called the *postsphygmic phase.* The ejection of blood into the aorta and the rise in pressure increases the pressure in the arterial system to a maximum. This maximum pressure is called the *systolic pressure,* while the minimal pressure which is held by the closure of the aortic valves is the *diastolic pressure.* It may easily be seen that systolic pressure depends mainly on cardiac output, while diastolic pressure depends on the condition of the aortic valves and the degree of vasoconstriction or vasodilation of the vascular bed.

Some of these pressure waves are projected into the jugular vein. There are three main positive waves which are called the *a, c, and v waves.* The *a or auricular wave* is a reflected wave of pressure produced when the auricle contracts, the *c wave* is produced when the ventricle contracts pushing the atrioventricular valves into the auricle and is due, also, to the wave in the carotid artery underlying the jugular vein. The *v or venous wave* is a stasis wave. It is due to the accumulation of blood in the jugular vein occurring during the time of closure of the atrio-ventricular valve. It falls when these valves open. The interval between the *a* and the *c* waves marks the time between the contraction of the auricle and the ventricle. It should not be more than 0.2 second, otherwise there is a delay in conduction.

The Electrocardiogram: The waves of excitation passing over the auricle and the ventricle produce characteristic electrical changes which may be recorded by suitable electrical apparatus. The P wave is due to the wave passing through the auricle while the Q-R-S-T waves are due to the ventricular events.

It would be beyond the scope of this book to go into a detailed discussion of the causation of these waves. It is sufficient to remember that *a P wave represents an auricular event* while the *Q-R-S-T waves represent ventricular activity.* The interval between the P and the R wave is an important interval for it measures the time of conduction between the sino-auricular node and the atrio-ventricular node. This time interval should not be more than 0.15 seconds. A longer interval is diagnostic of heart block.

Three leads are generally taken. Lead *one* is the lead using the right and the left arms, lead *two,* using the right arm and the left leg, while lead *three* uses the left arm and the left leg.

The Measurement of Systolic and Diastolic Pressures: The accepted method of measuring systolic and diastolic blood pressure is through the use of a pressure cuff around the arm, and the interpretation of certain sounds heard below the point of compression. If the cuff is inflated with a pressure greater than diastolic pressure, no sounds are heard. When the cuff is deflated and the pressure in the cuff equals or is slightly less than systolic pressure, the first sound appears. At further lowering of the pressure in the cuff, this sound becomes louder (phase 1), becomes muffled (phase 2), becomes clear again (phase 3), then muffled (phase 4), and disappears (phase 5). The change between the second clear sound (phase 3) and the muffling of this sound (phase 4) is taken as diastolic pressure.

The Cardiac Output: Several methods have been devised to measure the cardiac output. The value depends on the conditions under which it is observed. If obtained under resting conditions, in a comfortable external temperature and twelve to eighteen hours after taking food, the cardiac output is constant and is around 4.0 liters per minute. It is a function of surface area and is 2.5 liters per square meter of body surface per minute. Work, emotional excitement, food and alcohol increase the cardiac output. It does not bear a single relationship to the pulse rate for it is dependent on two variables, the force of cardiac contraction as well as the number of beats per minute. Normally the ventricle pumps out about 60 cc. per beat but its total capacity is 80 cc. Therefore, by increasing the force of contraction, 20 additional cc. may be ejected each beat.

Summary: **In this chapter a brief discussion of the circulation is given. The circulatory system must be very efficient in the aviator in order that he may withstand anoxia, cold and acceleration.**

Chapter XV

THE CONTROL OF THE CIRCULATION

It is obvious that there are times when the circulation must be speeded up to meet the increased need of oxygen by the tissues. Such times are during anoxia and muscular exercise. To meet this need there must be some mechanism present to control the flow of blood. As in the case of respiration, this control may be divided into *a neural and a chemical method of control.*

Neural Control of Circulation: The control of the rate of the beat is dependent on two sets of nerves, *the vagi* and *the sympathetic*. If the former are stimulated, the heart slows, if the latter is stimulated, the rate is increased. The right vagal endings terminate in the sino-auricular node, and the left connect with the atrio-ventricular node. Therefore, stimulation of the right vagus has more effect on the auricle while similar stimulation of the left vagus has greater ventricular effect. Stimulation of the sympathetic fibers going to the heart cause an increase in rate, but cutting of these fibers causes a slowing of the heart through the unopposed vagal action.

Vasomotor Nerves: Another form of neural control is through the vasomotor nerves. These nerves can be divided into those which constrict, the *vasoconstrictors* and those which dilate, the *vasodilators*. The vasoconstrictors are tonically active for if the splanchnic nerves are cut, there is a marked fall in blood pressure due to the vasodilation in the abdominal organs. Vasoconstrictor nerves go to all organs while dilator fibers have been demonstrated for the head, heart, pelvic organs and muscles.

Vasomotor Centers: Controlling the vasomotor nerves are two centers in the medulla, one affecting the vasoconstrictor fibers, and the other affecting the vasodilator fibers. The vasoconstrictor center which is tonically active for destruction of this region causes a maximal fall in blood pressure. The vasodilator center, on the other hand, only responds on stimulation. These two centers are, in turn, affected by impulses coming down from the hypothalamus and other regions of the brain.

Reflex Action: Impulses reaching the vasomotor centers may cause a rise or fall in blood pressure depending on the strength of stimulation and on the condition of the animal. Therefore, there are *pressor* as well as *depressor* reflexes. Heat generally causes a depressor response while cold causes a pressor. If these reflexes are so graded there may be no marked change in blood pressure. For example, during muscular exercise, there is vasodilation in the skeletal muscles and vasoconstriction in the splanchnic regions. The vasoconstriction of the splanchnic area causes blood to be shunted into the dilated vessels in the muscles and the net result may give only a very small change in blood pressure.

In addition to afferent stimuli, such as heat, cold and pain, causing changes in blood pressure, there are two sets of specialized nerve fibers which affect blood pressure. These are the fibers running with the vagus coming from the arch of the aorta and the carotid sinus. Since stimulation of the first group always produces a fall in blood pressure, the name, "depressor nerve" has been applied to this nerve. When this nerve is stimulated, impulses pass to the vasomotor center causing vasodilation of the splanchnic vessels as a result. Therefore, when there is a rise in blood pressure in the aorta there is a fall in the periphery. This reflex aids in the maintenance of normal blood pressure.

The nerve endings in the adventitia of the carotid sinus, also, respond to pressure. A rise in blood pressure in the carotid sinus causes a fall in blood pressure in the periphery, while a fall in blood pressure in this sinus causes a rise of blood pressure in the peripheral vessels. The reflex pathway is by way of the carotid sinus, through a branch of the glossopharyngeal nerve to the vasomotor centers and then out through the vasoconstrictor fibers. These latter fibers seem to play more of a rôle in the efferent pathway than the vasodilator fibers.

There is, also, a reflex mechanism which is stimulated by a change in venous pressure. The nerve endings which are stimulated are situated at the junction of the great veins with the auricle. When venous pressure falls, impulses go to the vasomotor centers, producing a rise in peripheral pressure. This reflex would aid in maintaining blood pressure when the venous return is inadequate.

In addition to these specialized regions for the reflex control of blood pressure, there are afferent impulses coming from such structures as the Pacinian corpuscles in the intestines, from the muscles during muscular contraction and from many other places in the body.

Chemical Control of Circulation: In addition to the neural control of circulation, there is a chemical control. This mechanism is not as important as in the case of respiration, yet, it, nevertheless, may play a dominant rôle in some cases. The local production of metabolites, such as carbon dioxide and lactate, produces vasodilation. Anoxia will, also, cause vasodilation. Adrenaline will cause vasoconstriction of the splanchnic area and vasodilation in the muscles. An increase in carbon dioxide affects the vasomotor centers causing a rise in blood pressure through reflex vasodilation. Removal of carbon dioxide by hyperventilation causes a reflex fall in blood pressure. Anoxia first causes a reflex rise in blood pressure but, later, this control is lost and a fall results. This action is a direct one on the vasomotor centers and, also, to a lesser extent, on the carotid and aortic bodies.

Examples of the coordination of this regulatory system will be given in the chapters on temperature regulation, muscular exercise and the effects of acute anoxia on man.

***Summary:* The neural and chemical control of the circulation has been described. The more important is the neural control. The numerous sources of afferent impulses going to the vasomotor center and the efferent pathways are discussed. A knowledge of these reflex mechanisms is necessary for an understanding of the vascular responses to cold, acceleration, and anoxia in the aviator.**

CHAPTER XVI

THE EFFECTS OF ACCELERATION ON MAN

In flying, for the first time in his existence, man has been subjected to marked acceleration. Acceleration may be defined as a change in velocity. Velocity does not affect man. The earth is revolving at the rate of 64,800 miles per hour, yet man on the surface of the earth is unaware of this speed at which he is traveling through space. Sudden changes in speed, either through an increase or decrease, however, affect man tremendously. These sudden accelerations are found in aviation.

Definition of "g": In order to have a unit for a force exerted on a body during acceleration, the *gravitational unit "g"* is used. This is a force which will pull a body towards the earth with an acceleration of 32 feet per second. The relationship between this force, mass and weight is as follows:

$$M = \frac{W}{g}$$

Mass is a constant, while the *weight* of an object depends on the gravitational pull on that object. If mass is unity then the weight of an object is equivalent to one g. For practical purposes, the weight of a man may be considered equal to one g. If forces are exerted on a man which increase his equivalent weight six times, it may be said that the force of six g is exerted on this aviator. It is obvious that a weight hung on a spring will pull the weight down to a certain extent due to a gravitational force of one g. If additional forces are placed on the spring which pulls the weight and spring down twice its original distance, then two g have been placed on the weight and spring.

Maneuvers in Which g Is Exerted on the Aviator: The aviator meets these additional forces in power dives, spins, loops, in fact, in any maneuver in which there is any marked change in velocity. For example, in making a banked turn, the speed must be increased to increase the lift when the wing surfaces are no longer parallel to the ground. The effective force is the resultant of the centrifugal force and the weight of the man. In a properly exerted 80 degree turn, the effective weight of a man is increased by 5 g.

The maximal forces which are exerted on a man are during a pull-out from a dive. During the first part of a pull-out, the diving speed does not decrease materially at the time the wings are placed in a pull-out position. Therefore, the wings have a sudden lift far in excess of the weight of the plane. The change in lift is proportional to the change of velocity raised to the second power.

$$g = \left(\frac{\text{Diving velocity}}{\text{Stalling velocity}} \right)^2$$

Therefore, if a plane were diving at 240 miles per hour and was suddenly placed in a stalling position where the velocity was 80 miles an hour, the force exerted on the plane and the man would be 9 g.

$$g = \left(\frac{240}{80} \right)^2 = 3^2 = 9 \text{ g}$$

Another method of calculation is to use the velocity of the plane and the radius of curvature of the turn.

$$F = K \frac{V^2}{r}$$

This formula shows that *the forces are directly propor-*

tional to the square of the velocity and inversely proportional to the radius of the turn. High velocity and short turns produce the greater forces on the man.

By convention, *accelerations* are divided into positive and negative. Accelerations which produce force which affect the man in the direction from head to foot are called *positive;* when they affect the man from foot to head, they are called *negative.* It must be remembered, however, that forces may affect a man in any axis dependent on his position in the plane during the application of the force.

Signs and Symptoms in Acceleration in Man: Since positive accelerations are met more commonly than negative, they will be described first. The subjective symptoms depend on the degree of acceleration. At 2 g, there is an increase in the sensation of pressing on the seat, at 4 g, the legs and arms become heavy and can only be moved with effort, at 5 g, the legs and arms cannot be moved at all, the blood is felt to leave the face, respiration becomes difficult, there may be a loss of vision and, later, loss of consciousness. If the acceleration is increased to produce more than 5 g, all of these symptoms may be increased.

The objective symptoms mainly depend on the fall in blood pressure. This, in turn, depends on the pulling down and accumulation of the blood in the abdominal region. Return of the blood is hindered and the cardiac output falls. There is a rise of pulse rate which is dependent on the degree of acceleration. The degree of fall of blood pressure is, also, dependent on the acceleration. Blackout occurs before loss in consciousness. This may be explained in the following way: If the blood pressure drops below 25 mm. Hg., the intraocular pressure will cause the retinal vessels to collapse, while blood will still flow through the cerebral vessels. Therefore, sight will fail before consciousness. If the blood pressure falls to the region of the intraventricular pressure, then consciousness is lost.

Negative Acceleration: Since the body is being pulled down with 1 g normally, a negative acceleration to 2 g would mean a change of 3 g on the body. In the first section, negative acceleration was defined as that acceleration producing an effect from below upward in the pilot. The sensations, therefore, produced are due to the blood in the body being forced towards the head.

At 2 g the face feels congested and there is a throbbing of the temples. At 3 g the congestion of the face increases, at 4 g the intracranial pressure has increased to such a point that the pilot thinks his head will expand. There is a marked pull of the body on the belt and incidents have been recorded in which the belt has broken and the pilot was thrown out of the plane.

Individual Variations: Experimental work, done mainly in Germany, has shown that there is a marked difference in the ability of men to withstand the effects of acceleration. For example, in a group of 22 men, 11 of them could withstand 6 g before loss of vision took place. A few could only withstand 4 g, while some could endure 7 g before losing their sight. There is another factor that comes into such a comparative study; that is, the *time factor*. If these forces are subjected onto a man for a very short time, they can be withstood much better than for a longer time. Most individuals have experienced marked changes of acceleration lasting for short periods of time, such as jumping from a chair and landing on the ground. It is only when these forces are prolonged that they produce the symptoms described above.

Protective Devices: Numerous methods have been suggested to protect a man from the forces of acceleration. The most practical is for the pilot to lean forward. The lowering of the head decreases the height of the column of blood from heart to head, presses in on the abdominal muscles which increases abdominal tension and may decrease blood stagnation in the abdominal cavity. It has been determined that leaning forward will gain from 2 g to 3 g. Therefore, a man who would lose vision with 7 g in the sitting position, will be able to go to 9 g or 10 g in the crouched position. Abdominal belts, water pants and other methods of increasing abdominal pressure in order to reduce venous stagnation have not proven to be of much help in this connection.

Parachute Jumps: In addition to accelerations during flying, man is subjected to accelerations during a parachute jump. A free falling body in space falls according to the formula $v = u + gt$, v being the velocity in feet per second, u the initial velocity, g the force of gravity and t the time in seconds. This formula implies that the velocity would constantly increase with time. However, a man falling from a plane only obeys that law for the first few seconds of falling. Afterward, the wind resistance counteracts the gravitational force to such an extent that he falls at a constant rate of 120 miles per hour or 10,560 feet per minute. The rate of fall with a parachute depends on the altitude. At lower altitudes the rate is generally about 1,200 feet per minute. At 35,000 feet, it may be as high as 2,160 feet per minute due to the less dense air at that altitude.

If a man jumps from a plane going 300 miles per hour, his velocity for the first few moments after leaving the plane will be the same as the plane. It soon decreases and the terminal velocity is the same as the man leaving a plane at the top of a loop where his initial velocity is zero.

The effect of acceleration in parachute jumps becomes of importance if the man should jump from a fast moving plane and open his parachute at once. This would cause a change of velocity of such an extent that it may break the shroud lines or seriously hurt the jumper. However, after the jumper has reached his terminal velocity, he may open the parachute without fear of danger to himself from the force of acceleration.

***Summary:* In this chapter, there is a description of the effects of acceleration on man. These effects are mainly in the circulatory system and produce profound changes in the aviator during dive bombing attacks and fast maneuvers.**

CHAPTER XVII

THE TEMPERATURE CONTROL OF THE BODY

In the first chapter, it was stated that the temperature decreased with altitude until the altitude of 35,000 feet was reached. At this altitude, the temperature is approximately −55°C. Above this altitude, the temperature remains fairly constant at this low level. Therefore, the aviator at high altitudes is exposed not only to the lack of oxygen, but also to extreme cold. An understanding of the reaction of man to low temperature becomes just as important as a study of the responses of man to low oxygen pressures.

Temperature of the Body: The temperature of the body is generally considered a constant at 98.6°F (37.0°C). However, careful study of the temperature throughout the day and in different parts of the body has revealed that there are marked variations. The body temperature is low in the morning (97.5°F.), rises gradually throughout the day, finally reaching its peak in the evening (99.5°F.) and returns to its minimum the next morning. Therefore, there may be as much as a 2°F. variation in temperature through the twenty-four hours. The temperature of the internal organs may be 1°F. to 2°F. higher than the temperature of the mouth. Skin temperature varies considerably, depending on locality and on external conditions.

Regulation of Body Temperature: Although there are these differences in body temperature, the changes in temperature of the body are small compared to the fluctuations of external temperature. The actual temperature of the body at any one time may be looked upon as a balance between heat production and heat loss.

It is obvious that to keep the balance, there must be some method of regulation. The body has two methods: (1) *the regulation of the loss of heat (physical regulation)* and (2) *the changing of the heat production (chemical regulation).*

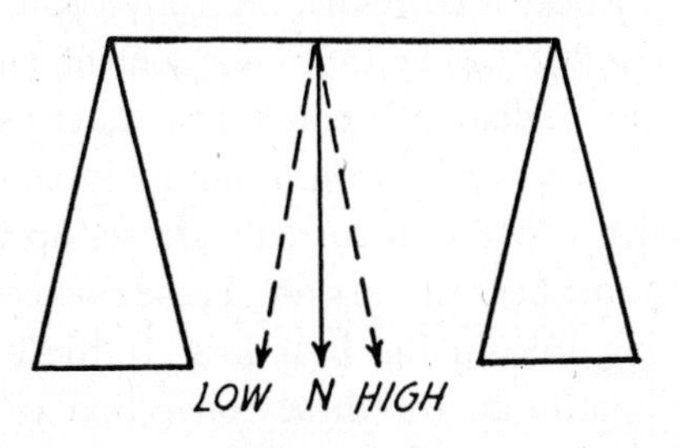

FIGURE 17

Heat production	Heat loss
Oxidation of	Radiation, conduction and convection.
Fats	Evaporation of water from lungs and skin.
Carbohydrates	Loss in urine and feces.
Proteins	Raising T of inspired air.

Physical Regulation: In Figure 17 the various methods of heat loss are given on one side of the balance. One of the main channels of heat loss is physical: through radiation, convection, and conduction. *Radiation* is the loss of heat through infra-red rays emitted from the body. *Convection* is the loss of heat caused by the passing of heat to the surrounding air, this factor depending mainly on the passage of air around the body. *Conduction* is the direct passage of heat from the body to another body with which it is in direct contact. The latter factor plays very little rôle in heat loss. We do lose a slight amount of heat by conduction when we sit in a chair. These three factors are influenced by the difference between the temperature of the body and temperature of the air, for the greater the difference, the greater the heat loss. This fact demonstrates that when the external temperature reaches body temperature, these three factors play no rôle in heat loss. Radiation, convection and conduction are, also, influenced by the water content (humidity) of the air. Infra-red radiation is reduced by water vapor, thereby decreasing this loss by radiation in humid weather. If the air is dry, however, convection currents are set up between this dry air and the air next to the skin. These convection currents may play a big rôle in the heat loss. If the outside air is moist, the opportunity for these convection currents is reduced and heat loss by this method is diminished.

Another important factor in heat loss is evaporation of water. It was stated above that when the external temperature reaches body temperature, radiation, convection and conduction cease as avenues of heat loss. If it were not for evaporation, man could not exist at external temperatures above 98.5°F. However, man has stayed in hot ovens at temperatures of 260°F. in dry air. The heat lost by evaporation of 1 cc. of water is 0.58 calorie. This heat is lost by the process of sweating and by direct loss through the skin. Under normal conditions of external temperature, heat loss by evaporation may be 20 per cent of the total loss, although in very warm climates it may amount to 90 per cent of the total loss of heat.

Heat is, also, lost by warming the inspired air, by vaporization of water in the expired air and through loss of heat in urine and feces. The relative portion of heat lost by the various channels is given in Table 16.

Chemical Control: When man is placed in a cold room, the tone of his muscles is increased and actual shivering may result. The shivering will increase metabolism and thereby raise body temperature. It is thought that a shivering center may be present in the hypothalamus. The thyroid gland may, also, be stimulated which would cause an increase in metabolism.

TABLE 16

HEAT LOST BY MAN DOING LIGHT MUSCULAR WORK AT ORDINARY ROOM TEMPERATURE

	Calories	*Per cent*
Radiation, convection and conduction	2100	70.0
Evaporation from skin	435	14.5
Vaporization of water from lungs	240	8.0
Warming inspired air	75	2.5
From urine and feces	45	1.5
Other methods	105	3.5
Total	3000	100.0

Neural Control of Heat Regulation: If a man goes into an extremely warm or cold room, he can regulate his temperature in such a manner that it does not vary within certain extremes of external temperatures. This is done by several methods. (1) *Redistribution of blood:* The skin vessels dilate or constrict. In cold temperatures, they constrict, thereby decreasing heat loss. (2) By *change in blood volume:* At low temperatures, blood-volume is reduced and the blood becomes more concentrated. (3) By *increasing metabolic rate.* These mechanisms are controlled by a center situated in the midbrain extending upward into the hypothalamus. Cold applied to this center causes a rise in body temperature while heating produces a fall in body temperature. This center is affected by afferent impulses from the skin and by the temperature of blood flowing through the center. It exerts its power through the sympathetic system going to cutaneous vessels, sweat glands, and pilomotor muscles, and may produce chemical changes through the thyroid and adrenal glands.

Reaction of Pilot at High Altitude: Man cannot withstand the extreme cold of high altitudes very long without external aid. However, he would attempt to meet this cold by marked vasoconstriction, rise in metabolism through shivering, decrease in blood volume, and marked decrease in loss of heat through evaporation. These mechanisms are inadequate and the man would die unless outside aid was provided. Therefore, it is necessary to meet this extreme change in temperature at high altitudes either by heating the cabin or by adding additional clothes to the aviator.

There are advantages and disadvantages to both systems. The advantages of the *heated cabin* are that the temperature of the cabin can be regulated to meet external need, and the activities of the men are not hampered by bulky clothing. The disadvantages are several: the external heat is dependent on a mechanical mechanism which may fail, there is formation of frost on the window surfaces and there is no protection of the crew in case the plane must make a forced landing.

The *addition of sufficient clothes* to meet this extreme cold has only one advantage, namely, the subject is independent of all mechanical sources of heat. However, the amount of clothing necessary to obtain adequate protection is so heavy and bulky that the man can hardly move. It is very uncomfortable at ground temperatures and has no means of providing ventilation.

There is a compromise, namely, *heating the suit.* This method has the advantages of the heated cabin and not the disadvantage of the unheated suit. The heating may fail and a heated suit does require a large amount of electrical energy. These are, however, engineering problems.

Reaction of Man to High Temperatures: Not only is the

aviator subjected to extreme cold while flying, but he also is subjected to extreme heat at sea level if operating from deserts or in tropical country. On carriers where ventilation during battle conditions is inadequate, pilots are exposed to discomfort from the hot humid conditions in their quarters. Therefore, a knowledge of the effect of heat on a man is of importance to the flight surgeon.

The Effect of Dry Heat on Man: In dry hot areas the relative humidity is so low that there is no limit to the evaporation of water from the body, regardless of the air temperature. Consequently, evaporation plays the most important rôle in the regulation of the temperature of the body under these conditions. In fact, the body may gain heat by radiation, convection and conduction since the surrounding air temperature may be higher than body temperature. Under these conditions the body may lose as much as 12 liters of water per day. With this water loss, there is a loss of sodium chloride. The content of this salt in the sweat varies from 0.1 per cent to 0.4 per cent. Therefore, when a man loses 12 liters of water, he may lose 48 grams of salt which is about one-third of his total sodium chloride content of his body. It is obvious that this man must replenish his water and salt content. If he does not, he will soon suffer from intense thirst, and if the thirst is not relieved, he will collapse and die. If water is obtained but not salt, the water will not be retained by the body and the man will suffer from heat cramps, serious weakness leading to collapse and death. Therefore, these men should receive one gram of sodium chloride per liter in their drinking water and at least 20 grams of sodium chloride in their food.

The Reaction of Man to Humid Heat: The above description applies to an aviator living in desert conditions. In contrast to these conditions are the humid conditions of the tropics or on ships. Under these conditions, the water vapor content of the air is so high that there is very little opportunity for the loss of water by evaporation. There is a slight loss of heat by evaporation but the chief loss will be by radiation, convection and conduction since the external temperature is generally slightly below skin temperature. Convection may be aided by the use of fans or forced ventilation. However, these mechanisms may fail and the body temperature rise. It is of interest that there is an individual variation among men for their ability to withstand heat. There is also acclimatization. These two factors may be used in the selection of aviators for their ability to operate either in desert regions or in the tropics. Preselection tests should be designed to select men for duty in the hot countries.

Summary: **A description is given of the regulation of the temperature of the body. The normal means of regulation are inadequate to meet the extreme cold of high altitudes. Therefore, either bulky clothing, heated suits or heated cabins must be supplied to the aviator going to high altitudes. The man's reaction to heat is also described, for aviators now operate in the tropics and deserts.**

CHAPTER XVIII

THE PHYSIOLOGY OF MUSCULAR EXERCISE

In the preceding chapters, a discussion of respiration and circulation has been given. This discussion centered around the changes occurring in these two systems in the resting man. However, man must work and work produces certain changes in respiration and circulation. It is important to understand these changes thoroughly. Although an aviator generally uses very little muscular energy in a plane, there are times when men in planes must use considerable muscular power, for example, when using a machine gun in a turret or when piloting a large patrol plane. In addition, it is necessary for an aviator to keep himself in good physical condition to withstand the stresses of flying. This condition can only be gained by muscular exercise. Provision must be made at every flying field for the aviators to have the time and opportunity for exercise.

Metabolism During Muscular Exercise: The primary effect of muscular exertion is to increase the utilization of oxygen. More energy is needed to carry out the muscular work and, therefore, more foodstuffs must be burned to meet this need. This demand for additional oxygen places the extra burden on the circulatory and respiratory systems to carry the extra oxygen to the tissues and the carbon dioxide away from the tissues. During rest, a man uses about 250 cc. (½ pint) of oxygen a minute. During work this value increases, the absolute amount depending on the degree of the exercise. When exercise starts, the oxygen consumption does not immediately rise to its final value. It takes several minutes before this value is reached due to the delay in the adjustment of the circulatory and respiratory systems in meeting the new demands. Therefore, there are three phases in the course of oxygen consumption during exercise, the *lag phase,* the *steady state* and the *recovery period.* The lag phase may last two or three minutes depending on the severity of the exercise. For greater degrees of muscular exertion, this part of the curve is steeper. Therefore, a man wishing to run at a certain rate in a short time should start out at a more rapid rate in the first few seconds of running in order to reach the steady state sooner. The second phase, the steady state, is the region where the need for oxygen in the muscle is met by the intake of oxygen. The magnitude of the steady state may be from 250 cc. to 5,000 cc. depending on the degree of the work and the ability of the man to carry oxygen to his tissues. However, degrees of work of more than 5,000 cc. can be carried out by man. This is done by the production of acids, especially lactic acid, which are oxidized after the work is over. Therefore, the body goes into "oxygen debt" to be paid back during the recovery period. Oxygen debts as high as 16 liters have been recorded. It can be easily seen that as the time of the work increases, the speed must decrease (Table 17).

TABLE 17

RELATIONSHIP BETWEEN OXYGEN AVAILABLE AND TIME OF WORKING

Time of work	1	2	5	10	20
Oxygen used during work	5.00	10.00	25.00	50.00	100.00
Recovery period	16.00	16.00	16.00	16.00	16.00
Oxygen available per minute	21.00	13.00	8.20	6.60	5.80

In the table, a calculation was made of the oxygen available per minute for various times of working assuming that the man can take in 5.0 liters of oxygen per minute and have an oxygen debt of 16 liters. The oxygen debt is a constant and depends on the man's ability to withstand acids in his body. If he works for one minute, he can work at a rate demanding 21.00 liters of oxygen; however, if he works for 20 minutes, he can only work at a rate of 5.8 liters of oxygen per minute. From these figures, it can be easily seen that a man running 100 yards runs at his maximal rate, but a man running 10 miles runs at his minimal. The 100 yard dash is made mainly at the expense of the recovery period; the 10 mile race is made in a steady state. The latter race is so long that man cannot depend on an oxygen debt but must oxidize all his metabolites completely during the race and, therefore, must adjust his speed to this factor.

Respiration During Work: In order to get more oxygen to the tissues during work there must be an increase in respiratory activity. This increase is so accurate that there is a definite relationship between oxygen utilization and respiratory activity, as measured by the amount of air passing in and out of the lungs per minute (Figure 18). The curve in Figure 18 shows that for an increase in the intensity of exercise there is a definite rise in respiratory activity. The increase in respiratory activity comes very quickly after exercise is started. In fact, the mere thought of exercise in some individuals will increase their respiratory rate and depth. The change is so quick that it cannot be produced by chemical changes, such as carbon dioxide production, but must be produced by nervous factors. Therefore, it is assumed that when impulses pass from the motor cortex of the brain to the muscles causing muscular contraction, impulses, also, pass from the cortex of the brain to the respiratory system causing an increase in respiration. These impulses play a great rôle in the maintenance of the augmentation of respiration during exercise. In addition, however, numerous other factors come into play in this connection. The increase in carbon dioxide, the production of lactic acid if exercise is very severe, the liberation of adrenaline the change in body temperature may increase the respiratory effort. The combination of stimuli,

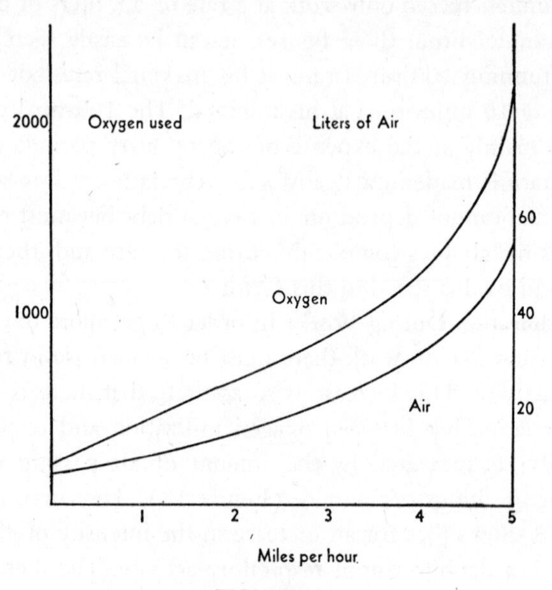

FIGURE 18

Oxygen used and amount of air breathed while working at various speeds. Abscissa, rate of walking in miles per hour; ordinates, oxygen used, in cc. per minute (upper curve), and air breathed in liters per minute (lower curve).

regardless of their exact nature, is sufficient to meet the need for extra oxygen during exercise in the maximal capacity of the lungs to take in outside air. The average maximal capacity is about 80 liters per minute although volumes as high as 120 liters have been recorded.

Starling's Law of the Heart

Circulatory Changes During Exercise: In addition to the respiratory changes there are marked circulatory changes. It is common experience that the heart beats more rapidly during exercise. It is obvious that if the circulation time of blood is increased, more units of blood carrying oxygen will reach the tissues per minute and, therefore, the supply of oxygen to the tissues will be increased. Numerous measurements of cardiac output have shown that the amount of blood pumped out per minute by the heart increases with the need for extra oxygen during exercise. This increase in the output of the heart is produced by two factors: (1) increase in the strength of each beat and (2) increase in the number of beats. Normally the ventricle pumps out about 60 cc. of blood per beat. However, the total volume of the ventricle is 80 cc. If the rate is 70 and the output per beat is 60, 4,200 cc. will be pumped out per minute. However, if the output per beat is increased to 80, and the rate remains the same, 70, then 5,600 cc. will be pumped out per minute. The greater factor, however, is an increase in the pulse rate. If, in the example given above, the pulse rate is taken as 150 and the output per beat 80 cc., the output per minute now has been augmented to 12,000 cc. Thus, both factors aid in this increase in cardiac output. The force of each contraction is dependent on the amount of blood flowing into the ventricle (Starling's Law of the Heart). With the increase in the pumping action of the skeletal muscles,* there is an increase in venous return. This increase soon augments ventricular inflow which stretches the fibers of the ventricle causing a stronger contraction. of the "Pressure Pump"

The increase in pulse rate during exercise is produced by several factors. There is a decrease in vagal tone and an increase in sympathetic activity. These factors come on so quickly that the first cardiac cycle after starting the exercise is

* Also of the "Axillary Heart," Watson, M.D.
"Venous Heart" i.e. chest and diaphragm
"Complemental Heart"
"Suction Pump"

shorter than the preceding one. The rise in venous blood pressure may also play a rôle. This increase stimulates endings in the right auricle which sets up a reflex mechanism to augment pulse rate (Bainbridge's Law). The liberation of adrenaline may also aid. These factors augment the pulse rate proportional to the amount of extra oxygen needed during exercise.

Blood Pressure: During exercise there is generally a rise in systolic pressure and a fall in diastolic. The rise in systolic pressure is due to the increased output of the heart while the fall in diastolic pressure is due to vasodilation of the vessels in the muscles themselves. There is a constriction of the splanchnic vessels which, in part, counteracts the fall in diastolic pressure produced by the vasodilation in the skeletal muscles. In fact, for light muscular exercise, there may be no change in diastolic pressure since these two factors may counterbalance each other.

Temperature Changes During Exercise: Another important change which occurs is an augmentation of the body temperature. The extra heat produced during the exercise is not completely lost. This augmentation of body temperature aids in the increase in velocity of all bodily processes.

Muscular Efficiency: In the true physical sense, the efficiency of any process is measured by dividing the energy derived from the process by the input of energy into the process.

$$\text{Efficiency} = \frac{\text{Energy output}}{\text{Energy input}}$$

The efficiency can be measured in man by having the man ride a specially constructed bicycle which measures the energy output, and at the same time measures the metabolism of the man in order to obtain the energy input. Results of this type of experimentation have shown that the efficiency of man is about 20 per cent. This value, however, depends on the speed of working. For very slow speeds, muscular effort is wasted in balancing. For very fast speeds, extra muscle effort is used in increasing the velocity of muscular movement. This factor has great application in industrial processes. The optional speed must be determined for muscular work in order to get the maximal efficiency for the man doing a job.

Muscular Training: A trained man can perform muscular work with greater ease than an untrained man and can work harder and longer than his unskilled companion. Several factors contribute to this ability. A trained man has greater muscular coordination and does not waste effort in purposeless movements. The pulse is slower and respiratory effort is less for doing the same job as the untrained man. The two latter factors give the trained man the sensation of comfort during work which would give discomfort to the untrained man.

Numerous tests have been devised to test the degree of muscular training in man. *The Schneider test,* for example, is used extensively for this purpose. It is sound physiologically for it gives a good score to a man with a low pulse rate, a moderate increase during exercise, and a rapid fall to the normal after exercise. There is a great deal of experimental evidence to show that these three factors exist in a well trained individual. A good score is, also, given to a rise in blood pressure when man goes from a lying to a standing position. This, too, is physiologically correct for circulation must readjust itself under these conditions. The chief criticism of this test is that the exercise is not severe enough. It does not cause a man to be pushed to his limit of muscular endurance in order that a real test may be made of his capacity for muscular work.

Fatigue: There are two types of fatigue: The fatigue which follows muscular exertion and the fatigue of mental work.

A combination of the two types is seen in aviation. Fatigue may be defined in terms of the result. There is a diminished capacity for work in this condition, whether the work be mental or physical.

The fatigue following muscular work is easy to explain in comparison to the fatigue resulting from mental exertion. In muscular work, the supply of metabolites may be exhausted, acids are produced and many other measurable changes occur. However, in mental fatigue, there is a diminished capacity for doing mental work. These changes are difficult to measure.

Fatigue is a common and serious symptom in aviators. The decreased capacity for work shows itself in men who take long trips in planes. The story is a complex one. There are many elements which produce the fatigue. Noise, vibration, inadequate food, nervous tension all contribute to fatigue on patrol flight. When planes fly at a higher altitude, the lack of oxygen, gaseous expansion in the intestines and cold may be added to this list. The effects of fatigue in aviators shows itself in the man's ability to handle the plane. Many theories have been offered to explain this fatigue state. None are satisfactory. There is no solution to this problem in aviation at the present time.

***Summary:* A discussion is given of the various changes in the body of man during exercise. These changes produce stresses on the circulatory and respiratory systems in order that more oxygen may reach the tissues. The development of an efficient circulatory and respiratory system through exercise aids the aviator in combatting anoxia, cold and the fatigue of flying.**

Chapter XIX

INSTRUMENT FLIGHT

By Lieut. Frederick B. Lee, USNR

Instrument flight is the control of an airplane without visual reference to external objects. In other words, it is the maintaining of a desired orientation of an airplane in space by a pilot whose visual reference is limited to the instruments in the airplane.

Such a limitation of the vision of a pilot can occur either in flight through clouds or fog or in night flying under overcast skies. In both military and commercial operations, the necessity for all-weather day and night flying and the development of radio facilities to permit such flying have made it a necessity that every pilot be skilled in instrument flight.

Contact Flight and Instrument Flight: In flight with visual reference to objects external to the airplane, or "contact flight," the pilot controls the airplane by changing its attitude with respect to some fixed point or line such as the horizon. Desired changes in the position of the airplane in height or direction come as a result of such changes in attitude. For instance, altitude is gained or lost by raising or lowering the position of the nose of the airplane with respect to the horizon, that is, by increasing or decreasing its pitch. An airplane will turn only if it is banked. Consequently turns are made by banking the airplane and holding the bank until the desired turn has been completed. The pilot therefore on contact flight learns to use the controls solely with reference to the visual indications of the airplane's attitude.

In instrument flight, the pilot is deprived of any direct indication of the attitude of the airplane, since the instruments upon which he must rely do not show the attitude of the airplane, but only the *results* of the airplane's being in a certain attitude.

For instance, every modern airplane is equipped with instruments which show the altitude and rate of change of altitude of the airplane. When these instruments indicate a constant altitude and a zero rate of change of altitude, the pilot can assume that his airplane is approximately level. If the altitude is changing, he must deduce from the rate of change of altitude how much the pitch of the airplane has been changed, that is, how much the nose of the airplane has been raised or lowered relative to the horizon. Somewhat the same information may be deduced by the pilot from changes in airspeed indications since the airplane's speed varies with its pitch. These indications of a change of pitch of the airplane come several moments after the change has occurred for the reason that any airplane has considerable inertia and does not immediately change its airspeed or altitude.

Likewise, the amount of bank of the airplane is indicated only indirectly. It must be deduced by the pilot from the instruments which indicate that the airplane is turning and that it is turning at a certain rate.

Only one instrument on the usual instrument panel, the gyro horizon, indicates the pitch and bank of the airplane. This instrument is designed to create the illusion that the pilot is controlling a miniature airplane, which is in an attitude with respect to a gyro stabilized artificial horizon similar to the attitude of the actual airplane with respect to the real horizon. The problems of instrument flight would be greatly simplified if complete reliance could be placed on this instrument. Unfortunately, the gyro horizon is not operative in all attitudes of flight, especially the extreme attitudes adopted in military maneuvers. Hence, every pilot must acquire proficiency in the use of the other instruments on the panel and in interpreting their secondary indications in terms of the attitude of the airplane.

Learning to Fly by Instruments: The development of skill in instrument flying requires that the pilot not only interpret the instrument indications of changing altitude, speed and direction correctly, but that he use this information to manipulate the controls of the airplane so as to obtain any desired attitude of flight. The pilot must use his controls in response to these instrument indications instantaneously and without reflection. His reactions can only be conditioned by intensive training and by constant practice.

The training consists of familiarizing the student pilot with the instrument indications for common attitudes of flight, and then teaching him how to obtain these indications by manipulation of the controls. The student does not have to be taught an entirely new technique of controlling the airplane, since control is essentially the same whether the student pilot is flying on contact or on instruments. The difference comes in the fact that on contact flight the plane may be controlled by changes in attitude which are seen directly and immediately. On instrument flight, the plane must be controlled by reference to changes in attitude which are indicated indirectly and, above all, are indicated some moments after the changes in attitude occur.

The student must first learn to fly the airplane in a constant attitude of flight, learning to hold the instrument indications steady. He may then learn to maneuver the airplane and to interpret the changing instrument indications in terms of attitudes of pitch or bank which the airplane has already assumed.

A student pilot may be taught the elements of instrument

flight control in two weeks. Many weeks of practice are required, however, for a pilot to fly on instruments without conscious mental effort. Once the skill has been acquired, it may be retained only by continual practice. Insufficient training or practice results in the pilot having consciously to think about each movement that he makes. This, in turn, results in extreme fatigue in a short period of time. Such fatigue eventually slows up the reactions of the pilot to such an extent that he may lose control of his airplane.

Orientation Is Maintained by Sight Alone: Every pilot must learn that *all senses other than that of vision are unreliable.*

In contact flight, the pilot uses the visual indications of the attitude of the airplane to maintain his orientation in space. The visual sense is so strong that it suppresses all other sensations in the pilot's mind and, as a result, he is not conscious of having any other sensations as long as he can see some fixed reference point.

When the external reference point is no longer available, the other sensations to which the pilot may be subject immediately come to the fore in his mind. Since these sensations are usually false, he will shortly become disorientated and feel that the airplane is doing unexpected maneuvers, even though the instrument indications prove that the airplane is in the desired attitude. The inexperienced pilot will feel a continual conflict between his sensations and what his instruments tell him is true. Therefore, he must use conscious effort to act in accordance with the instrument indications and to suppress any tendency to react in accordance with his sensations. With practice the pilot will eventually suppress or at least unconsciously disregard his sensations in instrument flight, just as he does on contact flight.

An individual on *terra firma* commonly maintains his

orientation in space by (a) *vision,* (b) *sensations from the vestibular mechanism of the inner ear,* including the static organ and the semi-circular canals, and (c) *deep sensibility,* including muscle, joint, tendon and visceral sensations, and touch, pressure and skin sensations. The nature of the movement of the human body in an airplane and the forces acting on it, make all of these sensations, *except that of vision,* faulty to such extent that they will cause the pilot to become disorientated.

For ease of discussion, the sensations of the pilot are divided as follows: a) in relation to angular motion or rotation and b) in relation to linear accelerations.

Sensations of Angular Motion or Rotation: Man senses turning in any plane in space by means of the semi-circular canals in each ear and the vestibular mechanism. It should be recalled that there are three semi-circular canals located in each ear and that the three canals lie at right angles to each other. In the ampulla at the end of each canal, there are sensory hairs which respond to any movement of the endolymph with which the canal is filled.

If the head is rotated, the canal in the plane of rotation will move with respect to the endolymph contained in it, since this fluid has inertia. This will cause a deflection of the sensory hairs and a sensation of rotation.

Two factors are responsible *for erroneous sensations* from the semi-circular canals. The first is that, normally, angular accelerations of less than two degrees per second cannot be sensed. The second is that the fluid in a semi-circular canal will quickly accelerate and, in a uniform turn, will in a matter of seconds come to rest at the same speed of rotation as the canal itself.

The result is that quick deviations from a given straight path may be sensed, whereas slow deviations are not sensed.

Likewise, in a uniform turn there will be no sensation of turning, after the turn has been maintained a few seconds. The only sensations will be of an increase or decrease in the rate of turning which are interpreted by the mind respectively as a turn from straight flight in the direction of the existing turn, or a turn from straight flight away from the direction of the existing turn. *In brief, man will have no sensation of turning in straight flight or in a uniform turn. His only sensations will be of positive or negative angular accelerations in excess of two degrees per second per second,* which will be interpreted erroneously during a turn as indicating turning from straight flight.

Sensations of Linear Acceleration: The static organ of the ear and the deep sensibility together give man sensations of linear acceleration. Both of these sensations react to the totality of all linear forces acting on the body, including gravity and centrifugal force.

In flight, the same forces act on the airplane as act on the pilot's body. For normal flight, equilibrium can be maintained only by having the resultant of all forces on the airplane act along its vertical axis. Consequently, in a turn, the pilot will merely feel that he is being forced down in his seat by the resultant of the force of gravity and centrifugal force. It is therefore not possible to differentiate between the two forces as it is, for example, in a fast turn in an automobile on an unbanked roadway.

Sidewards accelerations in an airplane are caused by the fact that the airplane is skidding or slipping, due to improper use of the rudder. Such accelerations may be interpreted by the pilot as connoting a tilting of the aircraft or as being the result of centrifugal force. In actual practice such sidewards accelerations may be caused by improper use of the rudder in any attitude of flight.

Sensory Illusions in Straight Flight: Common illusions in straight flight under instrument conditions are:

1. That the airplane is flying along tilted or tipped in one direction or another.

2. That the airplane is rotating about one or more of its axes. In other words, that it is turning, or rolling, or going into a continually steeper climb or dive.

The sensation of the airplane being tilted or tipped is caused usually as follows: the airplane may be tipped or tilted in rough air quite rapidly and the pilot receives the correct impression of the attitude of the airplane. He then recovers so slowly that the angular motion is not perceptible and his senses retain the feeling that the airplane is still tipped or tilted. The impression may be so strong that the pilot will lean over to one side in an attempt to assume what he supposes to be the vertical. This is known as "the leans" and is one of the strongest and most commonly felt sensations in instrument flight. It will give false impressions of both bank and pitch.

The same effect, although opposite in sense, may occur when a rapid recovery is made from an attitude which has been slowly and imperceptibly assumed by the aircraft.

The sensation of turning about any one of the airplane's three axes comes from the fact that the fluid in the semi-circular canal is imperceptibly accelerated, with the result that the pilot has the impression of turning after straight and level flight has been resumed. For instance, the airplane may turn slowly away from the desired heading without the pilot sensing the turn. This turn, if gradually accelerated may be of such a nature that resumption of straight flight gives the sensation of turning in the opposite direction. The mental impression of turning then may persist long after the actual sensation has died down.

The same persisting false impression may occur in varying degrees with the rotation of the airplane about any of its axes. The resulting sensations of continued turning, rolling, climbing or diving are the most confusing in all instrument flight and frequently cause faulty control of the airplane.

Sensory Illusions in a Turn: Common illusions connected with turning in instrument flight are:

1. A feeling that the airplane is continually pulling up into a steep climb during the turn and, a feeling that the airplane is being pushed over into a steep dive on recovery from the turn.

2. A feeling that the airplane is not banked at all, or banked in the opposite direction.

3. A feeling, when the pilot's head is moved, that the airplane is being snapped around in a turn and is doing a roll.

The usual turn is entered into so slowly and is at such a slow rate of turn that there is no sensation of turning whatsoever. The so-called "standard rate turn" commonly used in instrument flight is at the rate of *three degrees per second.* At this rate of turning, the illusions of the pilot may be similar to those encountered in straight flight.

With faster turns, and especially with fast turns executed at high airspeed, the deep sensibility and the static organ of the inner ear give the illusion that the airplane is executing a loop. This is caused by the fact that *in a steeply banked turn,* the pilot is forced down in his seat by the resultant of the force of gravity and centrifugal force. The total force acting downwards on the pilot in slow turns is little more than the force of gravity but, with the increasing bank required for fast turns at high airspeed, the downward force on the pilot increases rapidly. The amount of this force is shown in the table on page 123 (Table 18).

TABLE 18

RELATIONSHIP BETWEEN ANGLE OF BANK AND FORCE

Angle of Bank	*Force on Pilot (X Gravity)*
30°	1.15
50°	1.56
70°	2.92
80°	5.75
90°	Infinite

Thus, in a steep turn, the pilot is forced directly downwards with considerable force and, since there is no sensation of turning, he mentally connects this force with that sensed when pulling up into a loop. This sensation is continuous throughout the turn. It varies in intensity with the degree of bank of the airplane.

As recovery is made from a steep turn to level flight, the lessened force acting downward on the pilot's body creates the illusion of extreme lightness and the pilot feels that he is pushing over into a steep dive. This in turn will cause the pilot to try to counteract the sensation by pulling up into a climb *which may be dangerously steep.*

Illusions as to the angle of bank or direction of bank also come from the deep sensibility and the static organ of the inner ear as a result of the airplane's slipping or skidding during a turn, due to improper use of the rudder. Slipping or skidding will cause the pilot's body to be forced to one side or the other, causing an illusion that the airplane is banked or is tipped in that direction.

If the pilot holds his head steady in a turn, he will have little sensation of turning. However, if he changes the position of his head for any reason, such as to look downwards in the cockpit, he will have the sensation of doing a rapid roll and of being snapped around in the turn. The reason for this is that the movement of the pilot's head into a different plane in space will place a new semi-circular canal in the plane of rotation and will cause it to be rapidly accelerated in angular motion, while the canal originally in the plane of rotation has a rapid angular deceleration.

Sensations During Recovery from a Spin: During a spin, the pilot is subjected to high rotational speeds. If the spin is continued for more than an extremely short period of time, the fluid in the semi-circular canals will become so accelerated that on recovery to straight flight, the pilot will have a very marked sensation of falling off into a turn in the opposite direction and consequently will tend to return to a spin or a tight spiral in the same direction as before. This strong sensation, and the fact that nystagmus makes close observation of the instruments difficult, renders spin recovery an extremely difficult maneuver requiring the utmost in self control by the pilot. *Consequently, no maneuvers should ever be engaged in under instrument conditions which could result in falling into a spin.*

Summary: **Instrument flight requires the development of entirely new reflexes upon the part of the pilot, based upon visual reference to the instruments in the airplane. These instruments indicate only indirectly the attitude of the airplane and their indications can be interpreted in terms of the control of the airplane only after thorough training and long practice. All sensations from the inner ear and the deep sensibility are useless in aiding the pilot to control the airplane; in fact, they must be completely disregarded and complete reliance must be placed on the visual indications of the instruments.**

INDEX

A

B

C

C (cont'd.)

D

E

G

H

I

L

M

N

N (cont'd.)

O

P

R

S

S (cont'd.)

T

V

THIS BOOK

PHYSIOLOGY IN AVIATION

By CHALMERS L. GEMMILL, B.S., M.D.

was set, printed and bound by The Collegiate Press of Menasha, Wisconsin. The type face is Linotype Garamond, set 11 point on 13 point. The type page is 22 x 38 picas. The text paper is 60 lb. White Fort Sanders Offset. The binding is Bancroft Arrestox B-4950. The jacket is 80 lb. Linweave Text, Dark Blue, Laid, Plate Finish.

With THOMAS BOOKS careful attention is given to all details of manufacturing and design. It is the publisher's desire to present books that are satisfactory as to their physical qualities and artistic possibilities and appropriate for their particular use. THOMAS BOOKS will be true to those laws of quality that assure a good name and good will.